Middle School
Math Solution
Course 3

||Skills Practice||

CARNEGIE LEARNING

501 Grant St., Suite 1075
Pittsburgh, PA 15219
Phone 888.851.7094
Customer Service Phone 412.690.2444
Fax 412.690.2444

www.carnegielearning.com

Cover Design by Anne Milliron

ISBN: 978-1-60972-888-5
Skills Practice

Printed in the United States of America
2 3 4 5 6 7 8 9 B&B 21 20

Table of Contents

Module 1: Transforming Geometric Objects

Module 2: Developing Function Foundations

Module 3: Modeling Linear Equations

Module 4: Expanding Number Systems

Module 5: Applying Powers

Topic 1
Rigid Motion Transformations

Name _____ Date _____

I. Translations of Plane Figures on the Coordinate Plane

A. Describe the translation needed to match each pre-image to each congruent image.

1. pre-image: Quadrilateral *RSTQ*
image: Quadrilateral *R'S'T'Q'*

2. pre-image: Triangle *XYZ*
image: Triangle *X'Y'Z'*

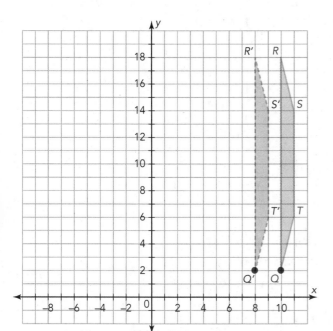

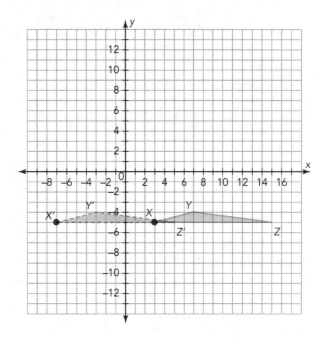

3. pre-image: Triangle *QRS*
image: Triangle *Q'R'S'*

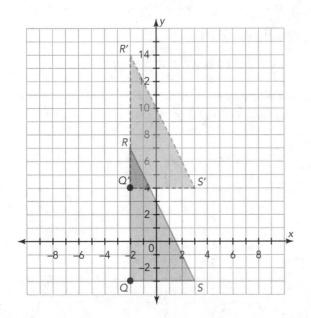

4. pre-image: Quadrilateral *WXYZ*
image: Quadrilateral *W'X'Y'Z'*

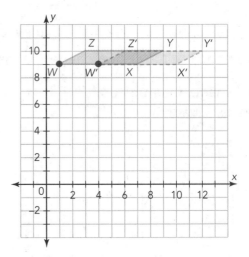

5. pre-image: Quadrilateral *QRST*
image: Quadrilateral *Q'R'S'T'*

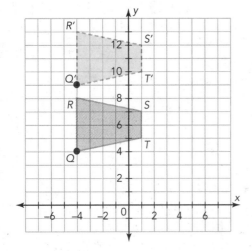

6. pre-image: Triangle *XYZ*
image: Triangle *X'Y'Z'*

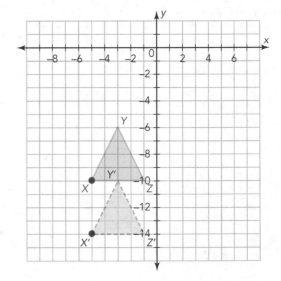

Name _____ Date _____

II. Reflections of Plane Figures on the Coordinate Plane

A. Describe the reflection needed to map each pre-image onto each congruent image.

1. pre-image: Quadrilateral *EFGH*
image: Quadrilateral *E'F'G'H'*

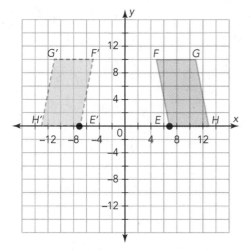

2. pre-image: Quadrilateral *WXYZ*
image: Quadrilateral *W'X'Y'Z'*

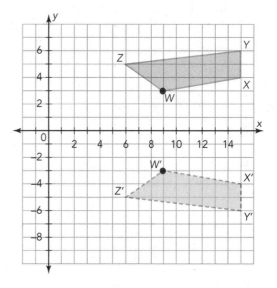

3. pre-image: Triangle *EFG*
image: Triangle *E'F'G'*

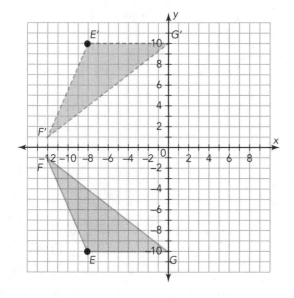

4. pre-image: Quadrilateral *WXYZ*
image: Quadrilateral *W'X'Y'Z'*

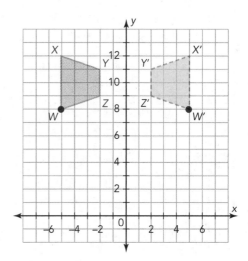

5. pre-image: Triangle *QRS*
image: Triangle *Q'R'S'*

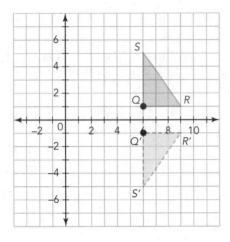

6. pre-image: Triangle *XYZ*
image: Triangle *X'Y'Z'*

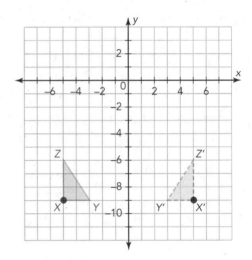

III. Rotations of Plane Figures on the Coordinate Plane

A. Describe the rotation needed to match each pre-image to each congruent image.

1. pre-image: Quadrilateral *ABCD*
image: Quadrilateral *A'B'C'D'*

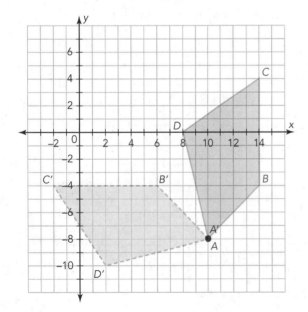

2. pre-image: Quadrilateral *EFGH*
image: Quadrilateral *E'F'G'H'*

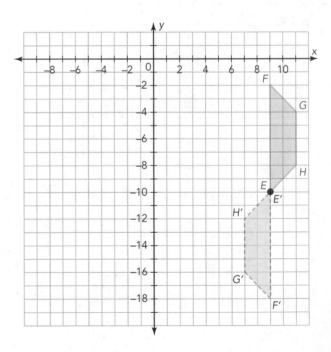

Name _____ Date _____

3. pre-image: Quadrilateral *EFGH*
image: Quadrilateral *E'F'G'H'*

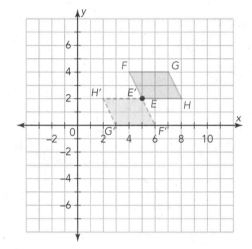

4. pre-image: Triangle *EFG*
image: Triangle *E'F'G'*

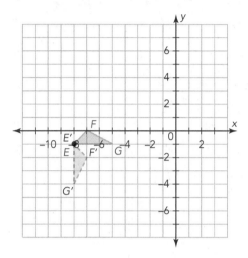

5. pre-image: Quadrilateral *QRST*
image: Quadrilateral *Q'R'S'T'*

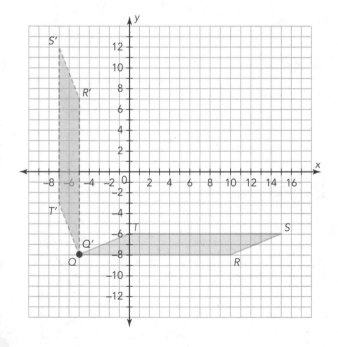

6. pre-image: Triangle *XYZ*
image: Triangle *X'Y'Z'*

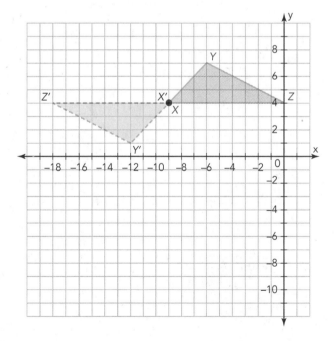

Topic 2
Similarity

Name _____ Date _____

I. Dilation of Plane Figures

A. Dilate each triangle using *P* as the center of dilation and the given scale factor.

1. scale factor: 2

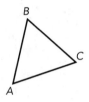

2. scale factor: $\frac{1}{2}$

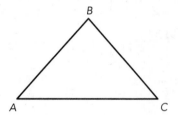

3. scale factor: 3

4. scale factor: $\frac{1}{3}$

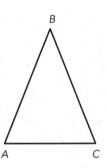

5. scale factor: 4

6. scale factor: $\frac{1}{4}$

Name _____ Date _____

II. Dilation of Plane Figures on the Coordinate Plane

A. Describe the dilation needed to map each pre-image onto each image.

1. pre-image: Triangle *ABC*
image: Triangle *A'B'C'*
center of dilation: *A*

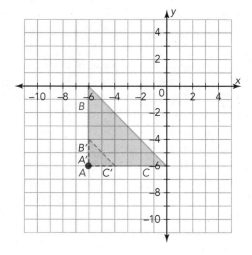

2. pre-image: Quadrilateral *QRST*
image: Triangle *Q'R'S'T'*
center of dilation: *Q*

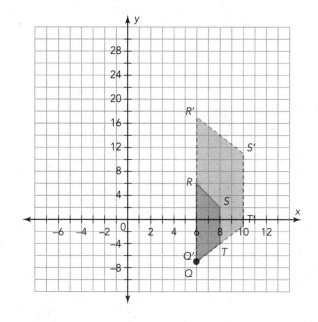

3. pre-image: Triangle *QRS*
image: Triangle *Q'R'S'*
center of dilation: *Q*

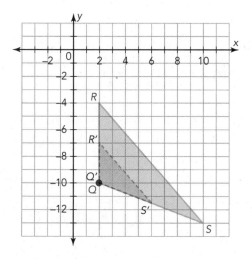

4. pre-image: Triangle *ABC*
image: Triangle *A'B'C'*
center of dilation: *A*

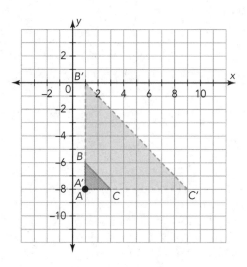

5. pre-image: Quadrilateral *QRST*
image: Triangle *Q'R'S'T'*
center of dilation: *Q*

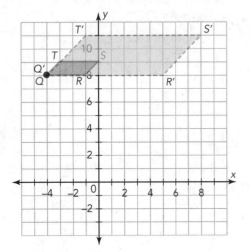

6. pre-image: Quadrilateral *WXYZ*
image: Triangle *W'X'Y'Z'*
center of dilation: *W*

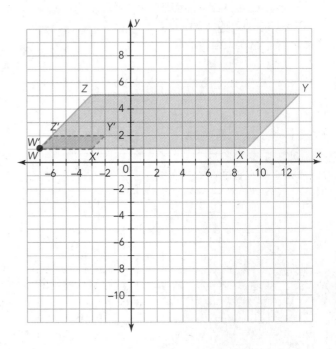

Name _____ Date _____

III. Combining Dilations and Rigid Motions

A. Describe the transformations needed to map each pre-image onto each image. Identify the center of dilation if possible.

1. pre-image: Triangle *XYZ*
image: Triangle *X'Y'Z'*

2. pre-image: Quadrilateral *EFGH*
image: Quadrilateral *E'F'G'H'*

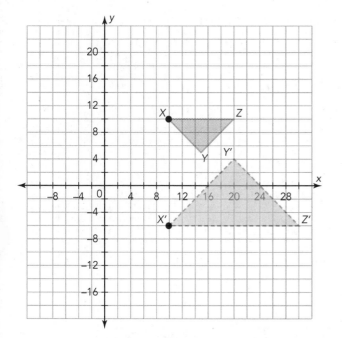

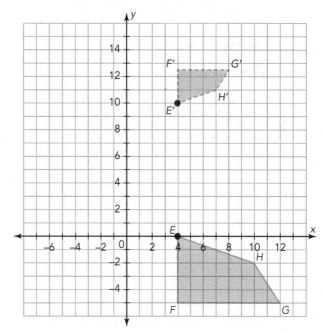

3. pre-image: Triangle *ABC*
image: Triangle *A'B'C'*

4. pre-image: Triangle *ABC*
image: Triangle *A'B'C'*

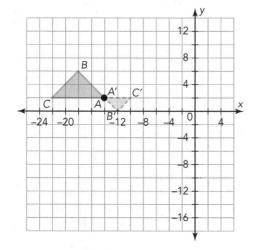

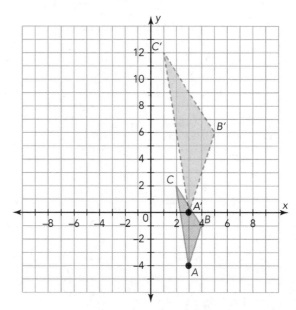

5. pre-image: Quadrilateral *QRST*
image: Quadrilateral *Q'R'S'T'*

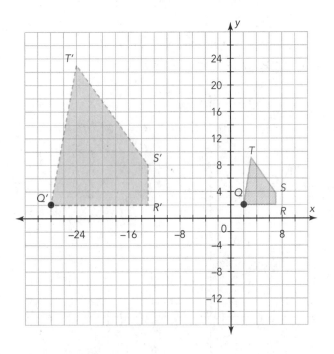

6. pre-image: Quadrilateral *ABCD*
image: Quadrilateral *A'B'C'D'*

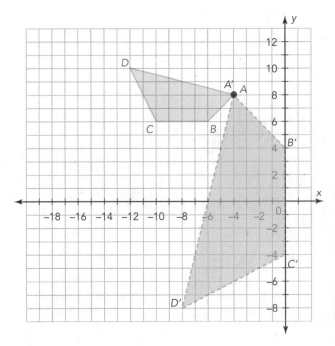

7. pre-image: Quadrilateral *QRST*
image: Quadrilateral *Q'R'S'T'*

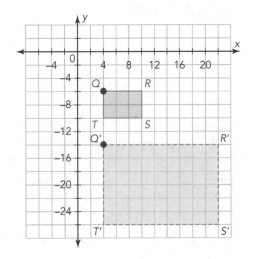

8. pre-image: Triangle *EFG*
image: Triangle *E'F'G'*

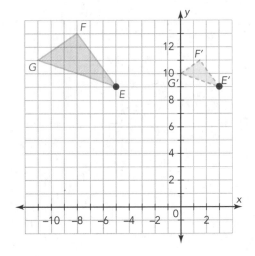

Name _____   Date _____

9. pre-image: Triangle *XYZ*
image: Triangle *X'Y'Z'*

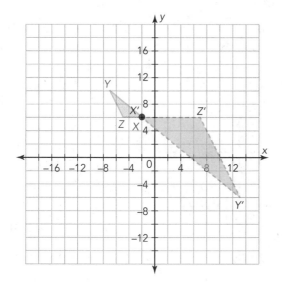

10. pre-image: Quadrilateral *ABCD*
image: Quadrilateral *A'B'C'D'*

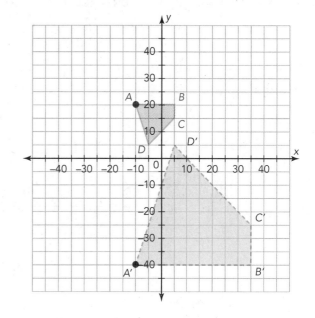

11. pre-image: Triangle *ABC*
image: Triangle *A'B'C'*

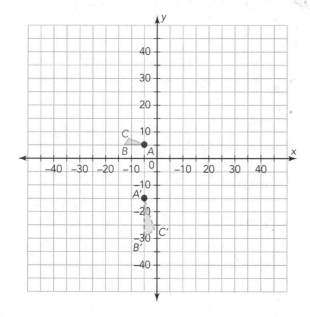

12. pre-image: Quadrilateral *WXYZ*
image: Quadrilateral *W'X'Y'Z'*

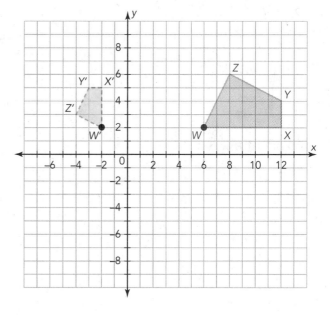

Topic 3
Line and Angle Relationships

Name __Adriana Ramirez__ Date 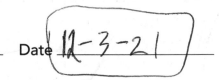 __12-3-21__

I. Classifying Angles Formed by Transversals

A. Use the map to give an example of each relationship.

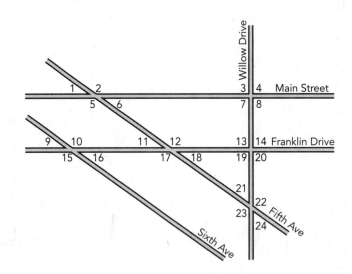

1. congruent angles

5,10

12,17

5,2

2. vertical angles

~~11,18~~ <11 & <18

2,12 9,16 <9 & <16

3. supplementary angles

11,12 1,2

9,10 5,6

4. linear pair

2,12 10-6-15

10,12

5. adjacent angles

22,24

21,23

6. corresponding angles

20,19

3,4

3,13

23,11

CHECKED

Name **Adriana Ramirez** Date **12-3-21**

B. Use the map to answer each question. Assume the streets extend beyond the edges of the map. Explain your reasoning.

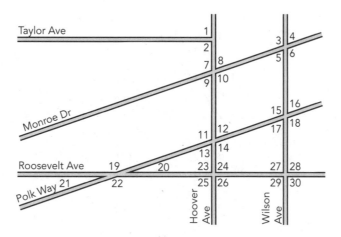

1. Identify each street that is a transversal to Hoover and Wilson.

Monroe Dr - Roosevelt Ave - Polk Way 21 ~~(MMMMMMM)~~

2. Identify each street that is not a transversal to Hoover and Wilson.

Taylor Ave ~~MMMMM~~

3. Identify each street that is a transversal to Monroe and Polk.

Hoover Ave - Willson Ave - ~~MMMMMMM~~

4. Identify each street that is not a transversal to Monroe and Polk.

Taylor Ave, Roosevelt Ave,

5. Identify all the angles that are same-side exterior to ∠11.

~~MMMMMMMMMMMMMM~~ <16 ~~MM~~ <25,

6. Identify all the angles that are alternate interior to ∠11.

<10, <17,

7. Identify all the angles that are corresponding to ∠11.

<15, <7 ~~MM~~, <23

8. Identify all the angles that are vertical to ∠11.

<14

C. In the diagram, transversal *t* intersects lines *p* and *q*. Classify each pair of angles as *vertical*, *linear*, *corresponding*, *same-side exterior*, *same-side interior*, *alternate interior*, or *alternate exterior*.

out   in

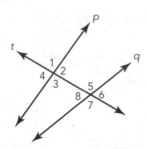

1. angle 1 and angle 2

~~vertical linear~~ Linear pair

2. angle 1 and angle 3

vertical ~~angle~~

3. angle 1 and angle 6

Same-side ~~Interior~~
          exterior

4. angle 3 and angle 7

corresponding
~~Supplementary angle~~

5. angle 2 and angle 8

alternate interior
~~same-side Exterior~~

6. angle 1 and angle 7

                exterior
alternate ~~interior~~

7. angle 4 and angle 7

          exterior
same-side ~~interior~~

8. angle 6 and angle 8

Vertical angle

9. angle 3 and angle 4

Linear pair
~~corresponding angle~~

10. angle 2 and angle 6

corresponding
~~congruent~~ angle

11. angle 2 and angle 5

Same side
interior

12. angle 3 and angle 5

~~corresponding angle~~
alternate interior

Name _Adriana Ramirez_   Date _12-3-21_

D. Use the diagram to answer each question. Explain your reasoning.

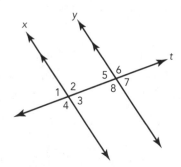

1. Identify the angles that are congruent to ∠6.

8, 2, 4

∠2 and ∠8

2. Identify the angles that are supplementary to ∠6.

∠IV and ∠III   1, 3, 5, 7

3. Identify the angles that are neither congruent nor supplementary to ∠6.

∠3 and ∠5   none

4. Identify the angles that are congruent to ∠3.

1, 5, 7

5. Identify the angles that are supplementary to ∠3.

2, 4, 6, 8

6. Identify the angles that are neither congruent nor supplementary to ∠3.

II. Calculating Angles Formed by Transversals

A. In the diagram, transversal *t* intersects parallel lines *m* and *n*. Suppose that the measure of ∠4 is 106°. Classify the given angle pair. Then determine each measure.

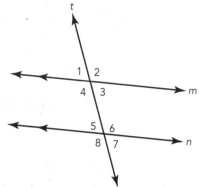

1. ∠4 and ∠1, m∠1 = 74° Linear

2. ∠4 and ∠2, m∠2 = 106° vertical

3. ∠4 and ∠3, m∠3 = 74°

4. ∠4 and ∠8, m∠8 = 106° corresponding

5. ∠4 and ∠5, m∠5 = 74° Same side interior

6. ∠5 and ∠7, m∠7 = 74° vertical

III. Angle-Angle Similarity

A. Use Angle-Angle Similarity and a protractor to show that each pre-image is similar to each image.

1. Dilate △ABC to form △DEF using point P(0, 0) as the center of dilation and a scale factor of 2. Show that △ABC is similar to △DEF.

2. Dilate △ABC to form △DEF using point P(0, 0) as the center of dilation and a scale factor of $\frac{1}{2}$. Show that △ABC is similar to △DEF.

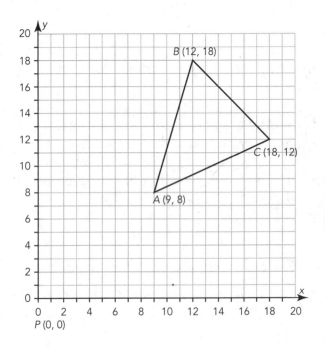

Name _____ Date _____

3. Dilate △*ABC* to form △*DEF* using point *P*(2, 3) as the center of dilation and a scale factor of 3. Show that △*ABC* is similar to △*DEF*.

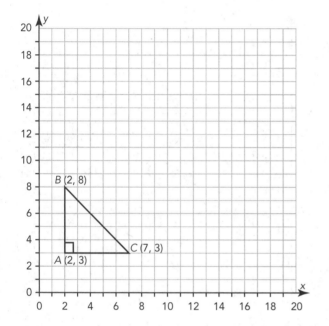

4. Dilate △*ABC* to form △*DEF* using point *P*(0, 2) as the center of dilation and a scale factor of $\frac{1}{3}$. Show that △*ABC* is similar to △*DEF*.

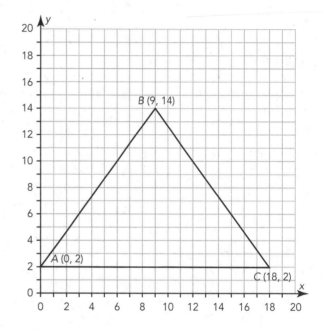

5. Dilate △ABC to form △DEF using point P(0, 0) as the center of dilation and a scale factor of 2. Show that △ABC is similar to △DEF.

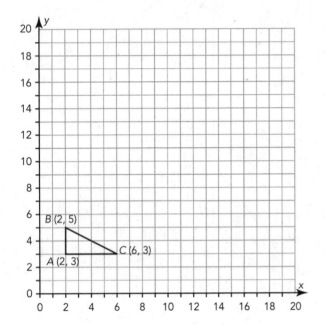

6. Dilate △ABC to form △DEF using point P (0, 0) as the center of dilation and a scale factor of $\frac{1}{4}$. Show that △ABC is similar to △DEF.

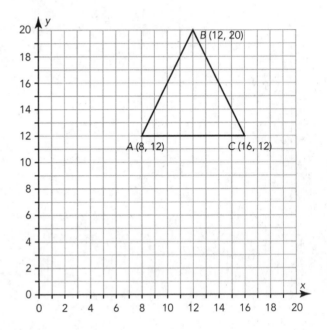

Topic 1
From Proportions to Linear Relationships

Name _____ Date _____

I. Modeling with Integer Rates of Change

A. Solve each problem.

1. Violet is trying to start an Intramural Club at her school. The principal tells her she must get signatures from students to show support. Each filled sheet contains 25 signatures.

    a. Write an equation to represent the number of signatures Violet gets given a certain number of filled sheets.

    b. The principal tells Violet she must have 7 sheets filled with signatures. If she fills all of these, how many signatures will she have in all?

    c. On Tuesday, Violet has 225 signatures. How many sheets has she filled?

    d. What is the unit rate in this situation? What does it represent?

2. Ada has started a business making doghouses. Her local hardware store saw her work and wants to buy as many as she can build for $45 per doghouse.

    a. Write an equation to represent the amount of money Ada receives given a certain number of doghouses built.

    b. Ada believes she can build 5 doghouses in a week. How much money will she receive from the hardware store if she meets this goal?

    c. Ada surpassed her goal and received $360 from the hardware store. How many doghouses did she build?

    d. What is the rate of change in this situation? What does it represent?

3. Marcos uses a fitness tracker to determine the number of calories he burns while running. He burns about 110 calories per mile of running.

   a. Write an equation to represent the number of calories Marcos burns given a certain number of miles he runs.

   b. Marcos runs 5 miles on Saturday. How many calories did he burn while running?

   c. After a run on Sunday, Marcos's fitness tracker shows he burned 385 calories. How many miles did he run?

   d. What is the rate of change in this situation? What does it represent?

4. Dr. Betz, a vet, is running a free rabies clinic for her town. She estimates it will take her six minutes for each animal she treats.

   a. Write an equation to represent the time in minutes Dr. Betz works at the clinic given a certain number of animals treated.

   b. After treating 11 animals, how many minutes has Dr. Betz worked at the clinic?

   c. Dr. Betz has been working at the clinic 1 hour and 42 minutes. How many animals has she treated?

   d. What is the constant of proportionality in this situation? What does it represent?

5. Elizabeth wants to increase the number of kumquat trees in her orchard, which she has divided into equal size units of land. Each kumquat tree will take up four units of land.

   a. Write an equation to represent the number of units of land used given a certain number of kumquat trees planted.

   b. Elizabeth plants 25 kumquat trees. How many units of land will be used?

   c. If one hundred thirty-two units of land in the orchard are used for kumquat trees, how many kumquat trees did Elizabeth plant?

   d. What is the unit rate in this situation? What does it represent?

6. Antonio works at the circus making balloon animals, charging $3 for a balloon animal.

   a. Write an equation to represent the total amount Antonio receives for a certain number of balloon animals made.

   b. Antonio sells twenty-one balloon animals by lunchtime. Determine the total amount of money he receives.

   c. How many balloon animals would Antonio need to sell in order to make $117?

   d. What is the constant of proportionality in this situation? What does it represent?

Name _____   Date _____

7. Russell will only read what he considers are "perfect books." A perfect book has exactly 350 pages.

  a. Write an equation to represent the number of pages Russell reads given a certain number of "perfect books" read.

  b. During July, Russell read 9 "perfect books." How many pages did he read in July?

  c. In August, Russell read of total of 5600 pages. How many "perfect books" did he read in August?

  d. What is the unit rate in this situation? What does it represent?

8. For each painting that Alita's art studio displays, she puts up two small signs interpreting the painting and presenting the painter's biography.

  a. Write an equation to represent the number of signs Alita puts up given a certain number of paintings on display.

  b. If there are 11 paintings on display, determine the total number of signs.

  c. Alita put up 52 signs around the art studio. How many paintings are on display?

  d. What is the rate of change in this situation? What does it represent?

9. Michelle works at a souvenir shop, where she earns $8 an hour.

  a. Write an equation to represent the amount Michelle earns given a certain number of hours she works.

  b. Michelle worked 25 hours this week. How much did she earn?

  c. If Michelle wants to earn $300 next week, how many hours must she work?

  d. What is the unit rate in this situation? What does it represent?

10. Autumn creates custom bracelets as a hobby and sells them for $7.00 per bracelet.

  a. Write an equation to represent the amount of money Autumn makes given a certain number of bracelets sold.

  b. Autumn sells 10 bracelets. How much money does Autumn make?

  c. Autumn has made $126. How many bracelets has she sold?

  d. What is the rate of change in this situation? What does it represent?

11. Hunter has lost his locker combination. It takes him 10 seconds to try each of the combinations he can think of.

    a. Write an equation to represent the number of seconds that have passed given a certain number of combinations tried.

    b. Hunter has tried 30 combinations. How many minutes has he spent trying combinations?

    c. It took Hunter five and a half minutes to open his locker. How many combinations did he try?

    d. What is the rate of change in this situation? What does it represent?

12. A computer keyboard manufacturer needs to keep track of the number of keyboards produced and the number of square buttons used in the process. Each keyboard needs fifty-five square buttons for letters, numbers, punctuation, and other functions.

    a. Write an equation to represent the number of square buttons used to produce a certain number of keyboards.

    b. An assembly machine produced 28 keyboards in an hour. How many square buttons were used?

    c. Another assembly machine used 3300 square buttons during production. How many keyboards did it produce?

    d. What is the constant of proportionality in this situation? What does it represent?

Name _____   Date _____

II. Modeling with Fractional Rates of Change

A. Solve each problem.

1. Stephen is making curtains for several windows in his aunt's house. He determines that he needs 8.5 yards of fabric for each window.

   a. Write an equation to represent the number of yards of fabric needed given a certain number of windows.

   b. Stephen counts 9 windows downstairs in his aunt's house. How much fabric will he need to make curtains for those windows?

   c. Stephen orders 161.5 yards of fabric for all the windows in his aunt's house. How many windows are in his aunt's house?

   d. What is the rate of change in this situation? What does it represent?

2. Melissa is given a bunch of nickels as her change after buying a snack. To figure out how much money she has been given, she starts counting the nickels.

   a. Write an equation to represent Melissa's total change in dollars given a certain number of nickels received.

   b. Melissa has counted 6 nickels so far. How much change is this in dollars?

   c. Melissa was supposed to get back $0.45 in change. If she received correct change, how many nickels should she have received?

   d. What is the constant of proportionality in this situation? What does it represent?

3. A citizen's group pays Ryan to collect signatures to stop a local park from being sold to an industrial developer. He earns $0.15 per signature.

   a. Write an equation to represent how much money Ryan earns given a certain number of signatures collected.

   b. How much will Ryan earn if he collects 60 signatures?

   c. How many signatures did Ryan collect if he earned $35.25?

   d. What is the rate of change in this situation? What does it represent?

4. Walter is swimming laps during swim team practice. He knows it takes him about 1.75 minutes to swim each lap.

   a. Write an equation to represent the total time in minutes Walter swims given a certain number of laps.

   b. Walter's coach asks him to swim 16 laps. How many minutes did he swim?

   c. At the end of swim team practice, Walter had been swimming for a total of 38.5 minutes. How many laps did he swim?

   d. What is the unit rate in this situation? What does it represent?

5. Takira is a translator who was hired to translate documents for a legal firm. In order to meet her deadline, she can only spend $\frac{1}{2}$ hour on each document she translates.

   a. Write an equation to represent the number of hours spent on the project given a certain number of documents translated.

   b. If Takira completes 14 documents on Tuesday, how many hours has she spent on the project?

   c. By the time she reaches her deadline, Takira has worked 19 hours on the project. How many documents did she translate?

   d. What is the constant of proportionality in this situation? What does it represent?

6. The Drama Club is selling small bags of popcorn at an outdoor movie to raise money for their club. The club raises $3.75 for each bag it sells.

   a. Write an equation that represents the total amount raised by the club given a certain number of bags of popcorn sold.

   b. The club sells 215 bags of popcorn before intermission. How much money did it raise?

   c. At the end of the movie, the club had raised $1200. How many bags of popcorn did it sell?

   d. What is the unit rate in this situation? What does it represent?

Name _____ Date _____

7. Maria plants a tree and waters it every day with $\frac{1}{3}$ gallon of water.

   a. Write an equation that represents the total number of gallons of water the tree receives given a certain number of days since being planted.

   b. How much water has the tree received 9 days after being planted?

   c. As of today, Maria's tree has received $5\frac{1}{3}$ gallons of water. How many days has it been since the tree was planted?

   d. What is the rate of change in this situation? What does it represent?

8. Ebony runs laps around the track at school. Each lap is 0.25 mile.

   a. Write an equation to represent the total distance in miles Ebony runs given a certain number of laps.

   b. Ebony has finished 8 laps so far. How far has she run?

   c. Ebony's pedometer says that she has run a total of 2.5 miles since she started running laps. How many laps has she run?

   d. What is the unit rate in this situation? What does it represent?

9. Coach Antonio is forming a baseball team. The tryouts are tough. The coach predicts that only $\frac{2}{3}$ of the players trying out will make the team.

   a. Write an equation to represent the number of players who are predicted to make the team given a certain number of players who try out.

   b. If there were eighty-one players who tried out, how many players are predicted to make the team?

   c. If the coach's prediction is true and twenty-four players actually make the team, how many players tried out?

   d. What is the unit rate for this situation? What does it represent?

10. Felix opens a brand new savings account to store money earned at his new part-time job. At this new job he gets a weekly paycheck of $140 and he plans to deposit $32.75 from each paycheck he gets.

   a. Write an equation to represent the amount of money saved given a certain number of deposits.

   b. How much money will be in Felix's savings account after he me makes 15 deposits?

   c. How many deposits will Felix need to make in order to save a total of $786?

   d. What is the rate of change in this situation? What does it represent?

11. For her consulting business, Joanna frequently drives to other cities to visit clients. Her frequent traveler pass allows her to pay a discounted toll rate of $0.10 per mile on the toll road.

    a. Write an equation to represent the amount of the toll bill given a certain number of miles driven on the toll road.

    b. Joanna travels one hundred eighty miles on the toll road. Determine her toll bill.

    c. On one trip, Joanna paid $6.50 in tolls. How many miles did she travel on the toll road?

    d. What is the rate of change in this situation? What does it represent?

12. Inez is the head coach of the Rockford IceHogs. She is trying to calculate the number of games the IceHogs need to win to make the playoffs. The team has not played very well this season and she predicts they will win $\frac{1}{8}$ of their remaining games.

    a. Write an equation to represent the number of games the team is predicted to win given a certain number of games played.

    b. If the IceHogs play 32 more games, how many of those games does the coach predict they will win?

    c. If the coach's prediction comes true and the IceHogs win five games, how many more games did they play this season?

    d. What is the rate of change for this situation? What does it represent?

Name _____ Date _____

III. Modeling using the Distributive Property over Division

A. Solve each problem.

1. Noah is going to purchase two items at an electronics store. The first is a computer for which Noah will be in debt for $550. He is still trying to decide how much he wants to spend on the second item, a printer. The bank has offered him 4 months of no interest. How much will he owe each month if he is in a 4-month payment plan, making equal payments each month?

  a. Write an equation to represent the amount Noah will owe each month given a certain price for the printer.

  b. If the printer purchase adds $170 of debt, how much will he owe each month?

  c. If Noah pays $160 each month by participating in the bank's plan, how much debt is added for the printer purchase?

  d. What is the rate of change in this situation? What does it represent?

2. The Harrison campsite has 10 volleyball courts. Every year, all the campers are invited to participate in a volleyball competition, but typically several of the campers opt out of playing and come to watch instead. The camp director divides the willing participants evenly among the courts where they decide who will play on what team. This year, there are 110 campers at the site.

  a. Write an equation to represent the number of campers per court given a certain number of campers who opt out.

  b. How many participants will be playing on each court if 40 campers decide to opt out of the competition and watch?

  c. If six campers will be playing on each court, how many campers opted out?

  d. What is the rate of change in this situation? What does it represent?

3. For the past 5 weeks, Santo has saved his allowance. He received 300 dollars in allowance, but he paid his little brother to do his chores for him.

    a. Write an equation to represent the amount Santo saved per week given a certain amount paid to his brother.

    b. If he paid his brother a total of $50, how much did he save each week?

    c. If he saved $42 per week, how much did he pay his brother?

    d. What is the rate of change in this situation? What does it represent?

4. You would like to find the average change in a stock value for 2 consecutive days. On Day 1 the stock decreased by $2.

    a. Write an equation to represent the average change in value given a certain change in value on Day 2.

    b. What is the average change in value if the stock decreases by $6 on Day 2?

    c. If the average change in value is a decrease of $2, what was the change in value of the stock on Day 2?

    d. What is the rate of change in this situation? What does it represent?

5. Your school is getting more balances to use in the science labs. The school already had 25 balances. All of the balances must be distributed evenly across the 5 labs.

    a. Write an equation to represent the number of balances per lab given a certain number of additional balances received by the school.

    b. If your school gets 60 more balances, how many will each lab get?

    c. How many balances would your school need to receive to reach the goal of 19 balances per lab?

    d. What is the rate of change in this situation? What does it represent?

6. Michael donates clay to his local school's art program. The school already has 65 pounds of clay. The clay is evenly distributed among 5 art students.

    a. Write an equation to represent the number of pounds of clay each student receives given a certain number of pounds of clay donated by Michael.

    b. If Michael donates one hundred ninety-five pounds of clay, how many pounds of clay are given to each student?

    c. How many pounds of clay did Michael donate if each student is given forty-one pounds of clay?

    d. What is the rate of change in this situation? What does it represent?

Name _____   Date _____

7. A local radio DJ has chartered 2 buses for a trip to the Rock and Roll Hall of Fame. The first one hundred tickets won their seats via a radio call-in contest, but the DJ is selling bus tickets to other interested rock fans. The DJ plans to distribute passengers evenly among the 2 buses.

  a. Write an equation to represent the number of passengers per bus given a certain number of bus tickets sold.

  b. If 56 bus tickets are sold, how many passengers will ride on each bus?

  c. If the capacity of each bus is 88 passengers, how many tickets can the DJ sell in order to fill both buses completely?

  d. What is the rate of change in this situation? What does it represent?

8. Mary breaks down paper products for a recycling company. Mary can typically break down about 100 pounds of paper in an hour. She had been given a large bin of paper products to work on this morning, but since she is only working part-time today, she gave 300 pounds of the paper to a co-worker.

  a. Write an equation to represent the time in hours it takes Mary to break down the paper products given a certain number of pounds of paper she started with.

  b. How many hours will it take Mary to process the remaining items if she started with seven hundred pounds of paper products?

  c. If Mary processes the remaining items in three hours, how many pounds of paper products was she originally given?

  d. What is the rate of change in this situation? What does it represent?

9. The Glenwood Lightning youth soccer team always has orange slices as their half-time snack. Another team had 12 orange slices left-over from their snack, so they gave the orange slices to the Glenwood Lightning. At half-time, the other team's left-over orange slices and all the orange slices brought by the parents of the team members were divided equally among the 8 players on the team.

a. Write an equation to represent the number of orange slices each player will get given a certain number of orange slices brought by the parents of the team members.

b. The parents brought 44 orange slices. Determine how many slices each player got.

c. If each player was given 6 orange slices, determine how many orange slices the parents brought.

d. What is the rate of change in this situation? What does it represent?

10. The waste water coming out of a factory is stored in a concrete pool where the sun can evaporate 7 tanks of water before Saturday. On Saturday, 2 identical valves are opened in the bottom of the pool to empty it into a river. Inspectors are interested in the amount of water drained per valve this way.

a. Write an equation to represent the number of tanks drained per valve given a certain number of tanks of waste water put into the pool before Saturday.

b. If 39 tanks of waste water were put into the pool this week, then how many tanks per valve were drained?

c. How much waste water would have to be produced to result in 12 tanks per valve drained?

d. What is the rate of change in this situation? What does it represent?

Name _____ Date _____

11. You are the bookkeeper for a small business. At the end of each month, you are required to total the amount of payments the business receives and distribute the money evenly to the 3 business accounts. In the first week of the month the business receives a total of $1260 in payments.

a. Write an equation to represent the amount of money added to each account given a certain amount of money received after the first week.

b. During the second week, the business receives another $1830 in payments. How much will be added to each of the businesses accounts so far this month?

c. At the end of the month, a total of $1430 had been added to each account. How much was received in payments after the first week of the month?

d. What is the rate of change in this situation? What does it represent?

12. Estelle is making 6 charm bracelets. She bought several packs of charms that she plans to distribute evenly among the 6 bracelets. However, after she opened the packs, she noticed that 24 of the charms were either damaged or broken.

a. Write an equation to represent the number of charms Estelle can put on each bracelet given a certain number of original charms.

b. If Estelle had a total of one hundred two charms to begin with, how many did she attach to each bracelet?

c. If Estelle uses thirty charms for each bracelet, how many charms did she start with?

d. What is the rate of change in this situation? What does it represent?

Topic 2
Linear Relationships

Name _____ Date _____

I. Calculating Slopes

A. Use the graph and the slope formula $m = \dfrac{y_2 - y_1}{x_2 - x_1}$ to determine the slope of each line.

1.

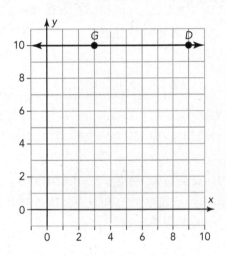

2.

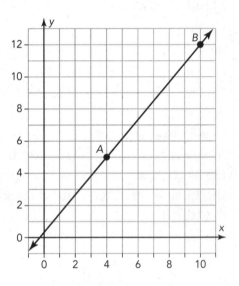

3.

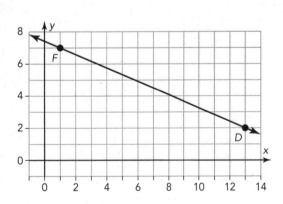

4.

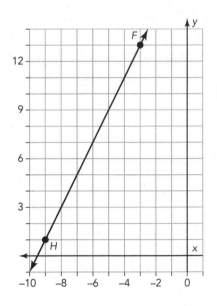

Name _____ Date _____

5.

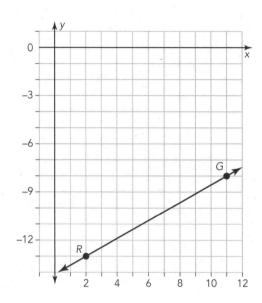

6.

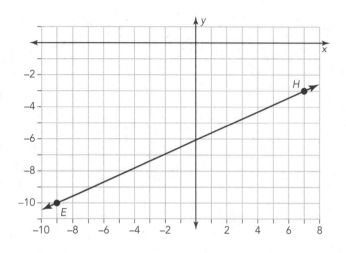

7.

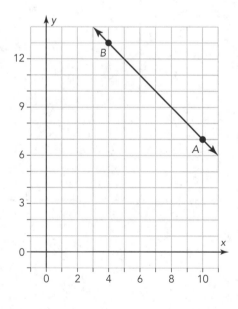

8.

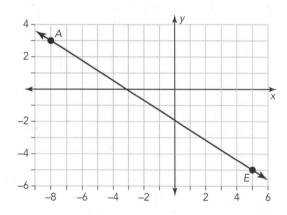

9.

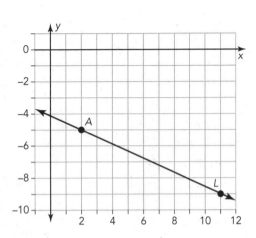

10.

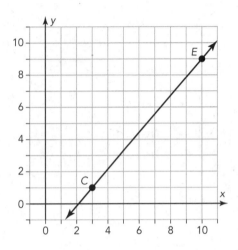

11.

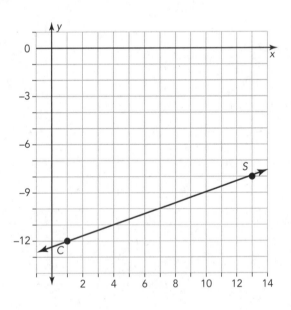

12.

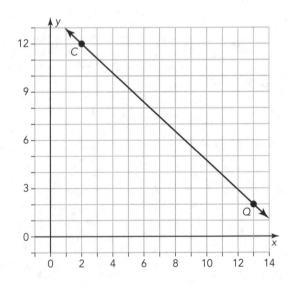

Name _____ Date _____

II. Graphing Given a Slope and y-Intercept

A. Graph each situation. Identify the slope and y-intercept of each graph.

1. At the beginning of the golf season, Karl buys 84 golf balls. He loses 2 balls each time he plays a game.

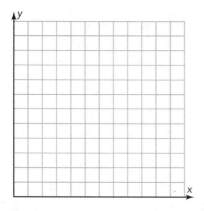

a. Write an equation that represents the number of golf balls Karl has left given a number of times he plays a game.

b. Graph the equation.

c. Identify the slope and y-intercept of the graph. Explain what each means in terms of the situation.

2. Frank averages a speed of 19 miles per hour during his bike race. The race is 60 miles long.

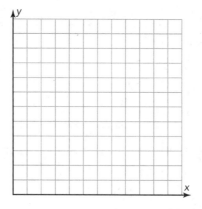

a. Write an equation that represents the number of miles Frank has left in the race given a number of hours he has been racing.

b. Graph the equation.

c. Identify the slope and y-intercept of the graph. Explain what each means in terms of the situation.

3. Jordan has a job delivering newspapers. Each Sunday, she earns $24.75 plus $0.20 for each house she delivers to.

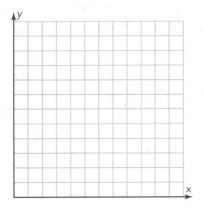

a. Write an equation that represents the amount Jordan earns on Sunday given a certain number of houses she delivers to.

b. Graph the equation.

c. Identify the slope and y-intercept of the graph. Explain what each means in terms of the situation.

4. Nakida read that the number of times a cricket chirps depends on the temperature of the air. The scientists found that the number of chirps per minute is equal to 0.23 times the temperature of the air, in degrees Fahrenheit, plus forty.

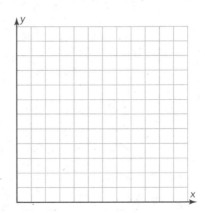

a. Write an equation that represents the number of times a cricket chirps given the temperature in degrees Fahrenheit.

b. Graph the equation.

c. Identify the slope and y-intercept of the graph. Explain what each means in terms of the situation.

Name _____   Date _____

5. Lenora is mulching her flower garden. She was able to mulch 48 square feet of garden before lunch. She plans to finish the job after lunch. Each bag of mulch covers 24 square feet of garden.

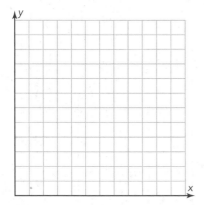

   a. Write an equation that represents the number of square feet of garden given a certain number of bags of mulch.

   b. Graph the equation.

   c. Identify the slope and *y*-intercept of the graph. Explain what each means in terms of the situation.

6. Susan and her band are recording a CD. After reading an article about great songs, they determine that each song they record should be about 3.1 minutes. The first song they record is 3.7 minutes long.

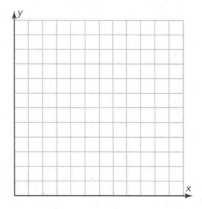

   a. Write an equation that represents the length of the CD in minutes given a certain number of songs recorded.

   b. Graph the equation.

   c. Identify the slope and *y*-intercept of the graph. Explain what each means in terms of the situation.

7. You are planning a training program to run a marathon. You start your program by running 5 miles per week and want to add 3.9 more miles to your program each week.

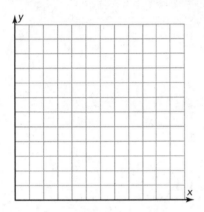

a. Write an equation that represents the distance you run in miles given a certain number of weeks.

b. Graph the equation.

c. Identify the slope and *y*-intercept of the graph. Explain what each means in terms of the situation.

8. Oscar is painting a canvas with one color that he will use as a background. He has already painted 5 square feet. The directions on his paint container state that each pint of paint will cover 16 square feet of canvas.

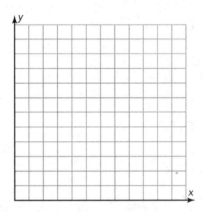

a. Write an equation that represents the number of square feet of canvas given a certain number of pints of paint used.

b. Graph the equation.

c. Identify the slope and *y*-intercept of the graph. Explain what each means in terms of the situation.

Name _____   Date _____

9. Shona just bought a new baseball bat. She expects the bat to last for 75 games. She plays 3 games a week.

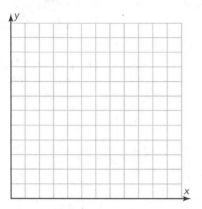

a. Write an equation that represents the number of games remaining given a certain number of weeks.

b. Graph the equation.

c. Identify the slope and *y*-intercept of the graph. Explain what each means in terms of the situation.

10. Latrell got a job paying $9.50 an hour at the coffee shop, but the first week there he spent $70.20 on smoothies, muffins, and frozen macchiatos.

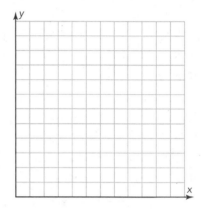

a. Write an equation that represents the amount netted given a certain number of hours worked.

b. Graph the equation.

c. Identify the slope and *y*-intercept of the graph. Explain what each means in terms of the situation.

11. Marcos is saving his money to purchase a smartphone. He already has $57 saved, and he saves $10 a week from his part-time job walking neighborhood dogs.

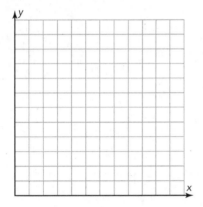

a. Write an equation that represents the total amount saved given a certain number of weeks.

b. Graph the equation.

c. Identify the slope and y-intercept of the graph. Explain what each means in terms of the situation.

12. The fire department is looking into reducing fuel expenditures this year when they are called to clear an area of trees. It currently use gas-powered chainsaws to clear the trees. On a typical workday, it purchases 48 gallons of gasoline. It finds that it uses an average of 6 gallons of gas an hour when using the chainsaws.

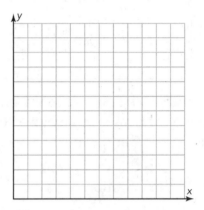

a. Write an equation that represents the number of gallons of gas left given a certain number of hours.

b. Graph the equation.

c. Identify the slope and y-intercept of the graph. Explain what each means in terms of the situation.

Name _____   Date _____

13. Your class is going to see a special
exhibition on reptiles at the science
museum. The ticket service company
bills your school $13 per student plus a
$9.95 service fee.

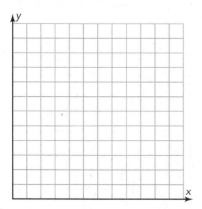

a. Write an equation that represents the
total cost given a certain number of
students.

b. Graph the equation.

c. Identify the slope and *y*-intercept of
the graph. Explain what each means
in terms of the situation.

14. Your school has a food festival each
spring. They charge a $6 entrance fee
and one $0.75 ticket for each item you
taste.

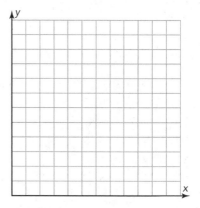

a. Write an equation that represents the
total cost given a certain number of
items tasted.

b. Graph the equation.

c. Identify the slope and *y*-intercept of
the graph. Explain what each means
in terms of the situation.

15. Lamar likes to photograph things in nature. He has just completed a collection of 34 plant photos. His next task is to find and photograph bugs. He sets out to take 5 bug photos each day.

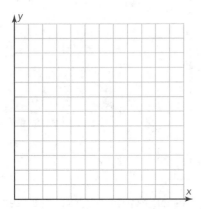

a. Write an equation that represents the number of nature photos taken given a certain number of days.

b. Graph the equation.

c. Identify the slope and *y*-intercept of the graph. Explain what each means in terms of the situation.

16. The are currently about 105 male wolves in Yellowstone Park. During birthing season, the average number of male offspring that are added to the population is about 0.51 times the number of wolves that will give birth.

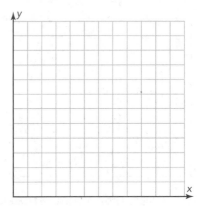

a. Write an equation that represents the population of male wolves given a certain number of wolves giving birth.

b. Graph the equation.

c. Identify the slope and *y*-intercept of the graph. Explain what each means in terms of the situation.

Name _____   Date _____

17. A polar bear weighed 0.5 kilogram at birth. Following its birth it gained 0.4 kilogram each week.

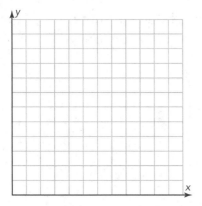

a. Write an equation that represents the weight in kilograms of the polar bear given a certain number of weeks.

b. Graph the equation.

c. Identify the slope and *y*-intercept of the graph. Explain what each means in terms of the situation.

18. Frank runs a business making curtains. For each job, he charges a $30 service fee for measuring and installing the curtains, and $9 per square foot of material needed.

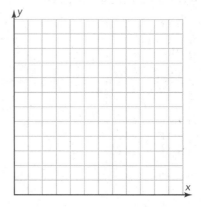

a. Write an equation that represents the total Frank charges given a certain amount of material.

b. Graph the equation.

c. Identify the slope and *y*-intercept of the graph. Explain what each means in terms of the situation.

19. In the early days of baseball, pitchers used only a few balls each game, but now pitchers change balls much more frequently. Every major league baseball game starts with 140 new baseballs. Every inning, an average of 9 baseballs is used.

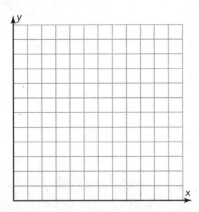

   a. Write an equation that represents the number of new baseballs remaining given a certain number of innings.

   b. Graph the equation.

   c. Identify the slope and y-intercept of the graph. Explain what each means in terms of the situation.

20. In order to maintain good health, it is recommended that girls from 14 to 18 years of age consume 9.1 grams of magnesium every 30 days. A 15-year-old girl has been consuming 0.31 grams of magnesium every day.

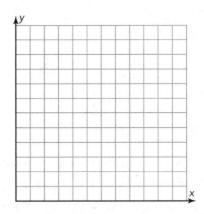

   a. Write an equation that represents the amount remaining to consume given a certain number of days.

   b. Graph the equation.

   c. Identify the slope and y-intercept of the graph. Explain what each means in terms of the situation.

Name _____ Date _____

III. Graphing Linear Equations

A. Use the slope and *y*-intercept to graph each equation.

1. Graph the equation $y = -3x - 6$.

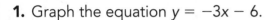

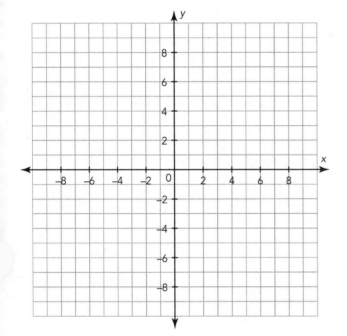

a. Determine the *y*-intercept by substituting 0 for *x*.

b. Use the slope to determine another point on the line. Write the coordinates of the point.

c. Draw a line to graph the equation.

2. Graph the equation $y = -2x - 9$.

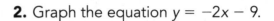

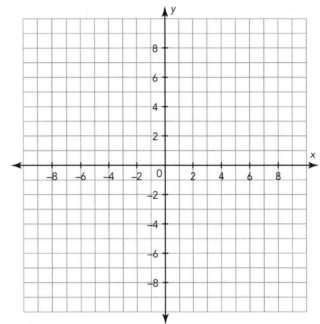

a. Determine the *y*-intercept by substituting 0 for *x*.

b. Use the slope to determine another point on the line. Write the coordinates of the point.

c. Draw a line to graph the equation.

3. Graph the equation $y = x + 4$.

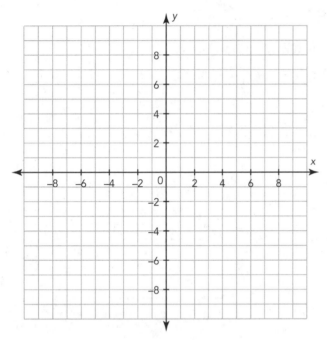

a. Determine the *y*-intercept by substituting 0 for *x*.

b. Use the slope to determine another point on the line. Write the coordinates of the point.

c. Draw a line to graph the equation.

4. Graph the equation $y = -8x + 9$.

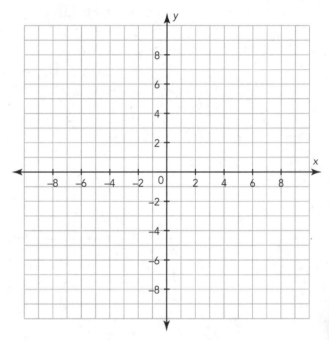

a. Determine the *y*-intercept by substituting 0 for *x*.

b. Use the slope to determine another point on the line. Write the coordinates of the point.

c. Draw a line to graph the equation.

Name _____   Date _____

5. Graph the equation $y = 2x + 5$.

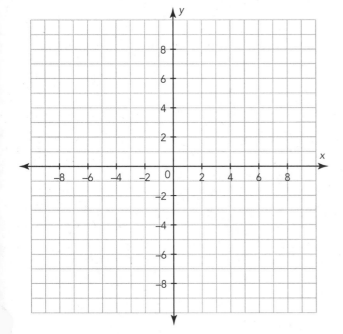

6. Graph the equation $y = -3x + 1$.

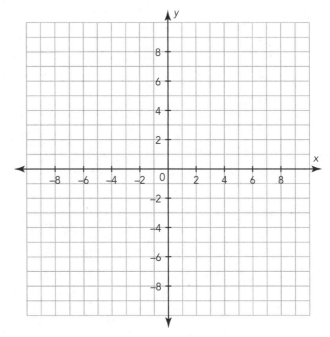

a. Determine the *y*-intercept by substituting 0 for *x*.

b. Use the slope to determine another point on the line. Write the coordinates of the point.

c. Draw a line to graph the equation.

a. Determine the *y*-intercept by substituting 0 for *x*.

b. Use the slope to determine another point on the line. Write the coordinates of the point.

c. Draw a line to graph the equation.

7. Graph the equation $y = 4x - 1$.

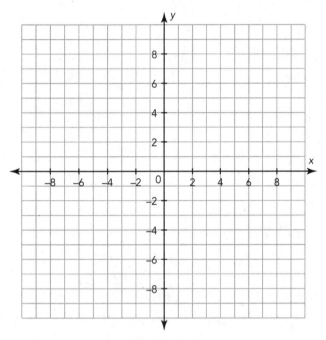

a. Determine the *y*-intercept by substituting 0 for *x*.

b. Use the slope to determine another point on the line. Write the coordinates of the point.

c. Draw a line to graph the equation.

8. Graph the equation $y = 3x - 7$.

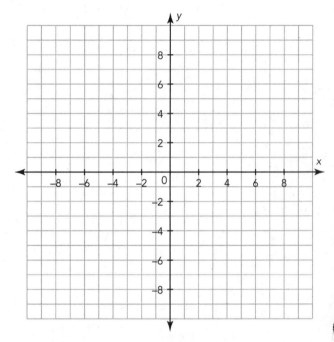

a. Determine the *y*-intercept by substituting 0 for *x*.

b. Use the slope to determine another point on the line. Write the coordinates of the point.

c. Draw a line to graph the equation.

Name _____   Date _____

9. Graph the equation $y = -x - 2$.

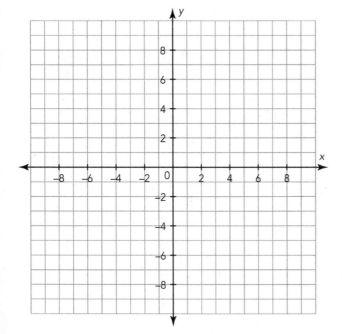

a. Determine the *y*-intercept by substituting 0 for *x*.

b. Use the slope to determine another point on the line. Write the coordinates of the point.

c. Draw a line to graph the equation.

10. Graph the equation $y = 6x + 4$.

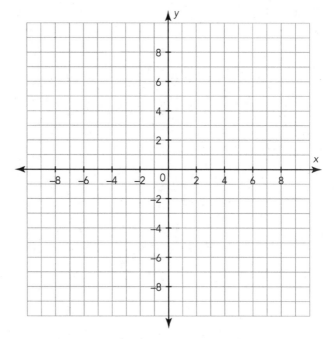

a. Determine the *y*-intercept by substituting 0 for *x*.

b. Use the slope to determine another point on the line. Write the coordinates of the point.

c. Draw a line to graph the equation.

11. Graph the equation $y = -5x + 4$.

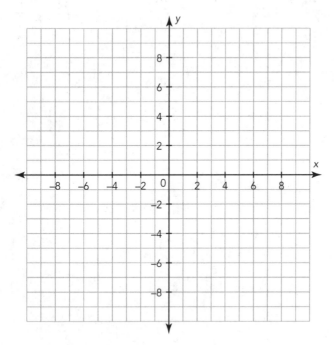

a. Determine the y-intercept by substituting 0 for x.

b. Use the slope to determine another point on the line. Write the coordinates of the point.

c. Draw a line to graph the equation.

12. Graph the equation $y = 7x - 4$.

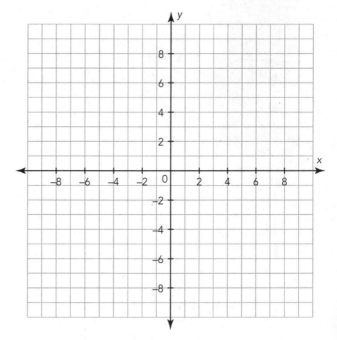

a. Determine the y-intercept by substituting 0 for x.

b. Use the slope to determine another point on the line. Write the coordinates of the point.

c. Draw a line to graph the equation.

Name _____ Date _____

B. Use the slope and a point to graph each equation.

1. Graph the equation $y - 2 = 2(x - 1)$.

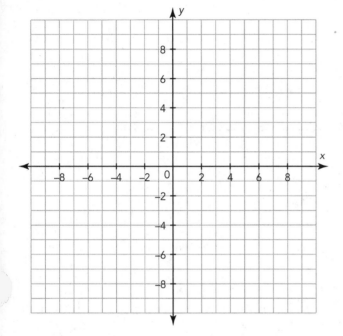

2. Graph the equation $y + 3 = -1(x - 2)$.

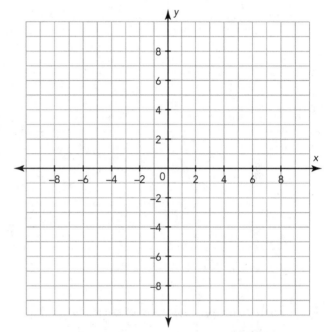

a. Determine a point on the graph of the equation.

b. Use the slope to determine another point on the line. Write the coordinates of the point.

c. Draw a line to graph the equation.

a. Determine a point on the graph of the equation.

b. Use the slope to determine another point on the line. Write the coordinates of the point.

c. Draw a line to graph the equation.

3. Graph the equation $y - 5 = 3(x + 1)$.

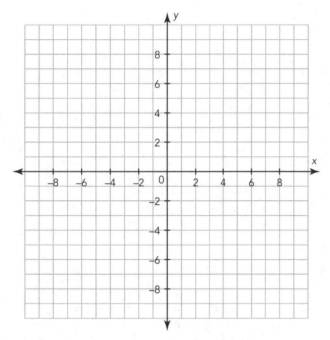

a. Determine a point on the graph of the equation.

b. Use the slope to determine another point on the line. Write the coordinates of the point.

c. Draw a line to graph the equation.

4. Graph the equation $y + 4 = -2(x + 2)$.

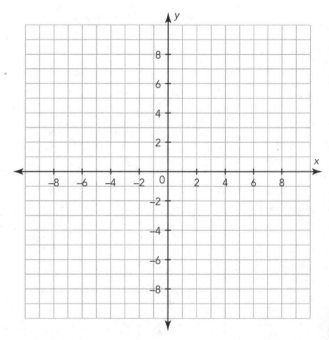

a. Determine a point on the graph of the equation.

b. Use the slope to determine another point on the line. Write the coordinates of the point.

c. Draw a line to graph the equation.

Name _____ Date _____

5. Graph the equation $y - 4 = -3(x - 1)$.

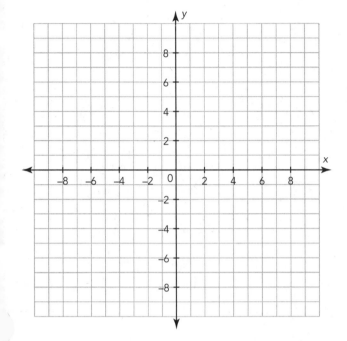

a. Determine a point on the graph of the equation.

b. Use the slope to determine another point on the line. Write the coordinates of the point.

c. Draw a line to graph the equation.

6. Graph the equation $y + 3 = 4(x - 3)$.

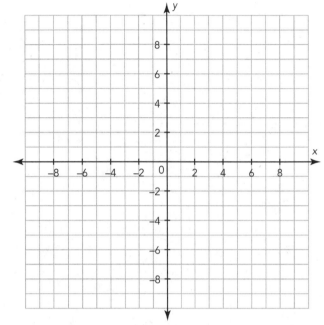

a. Determine a point on the graph of the equation.

b. Use the slope to determine another point on the line. Write the coordinates of the point.

c. Draw a line to graph the equation.

7. Graph the equation $y - 2 = -4(x + 4)$.

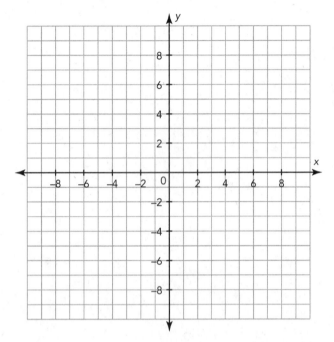

8. Graph the equation $y + 2 = x + 6$.

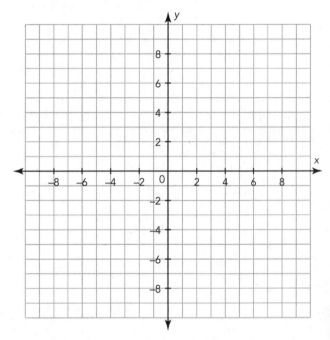

a. Determine a point on the graph of the equation.

b. Use the slope to determine another point on the line. Write the coordinates of the point.

c. Draw a line to graph the equation.

a. Determine a point on the graph of the equation.

b. Use the slope to determine another point on the line. Write the coordinates of the point.

c. Draw a line to graph the equation.

Name _____   Date _____

9. Graph the equation $y - 3 = -(x - 4)$.

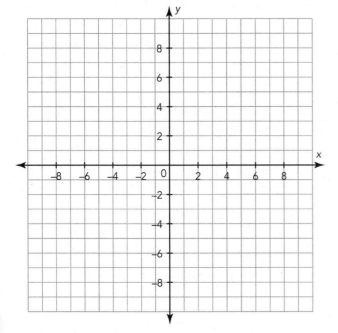

a. Determine a point on the graph of the equation.

b. Use the slope to determine another point on the line. Write the coordinates of the point.

c. Draw a line to graph the equation.

10. Graph the equation $y + 1 = -2(x - 7)$.

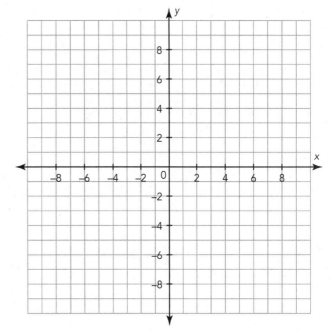

a. Determine a point on the graph of the equation.

b. Use the slope to determine another point on the line. Write the coordinates of the point.

c. Draw a line to graph the equation.

11. Graph the equation $y - 6 = 2(x + 3)$.

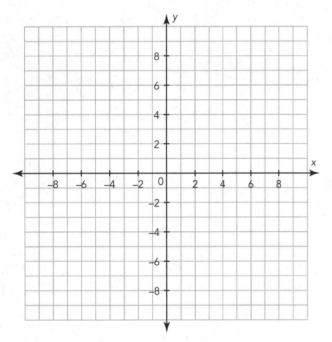

a. Determine a point on the graph of the equation.

b. Use the slope to determine another point on the line. Write the coordinates of the point.

c. Draw a line to graph the equation.

12. Graph the equation $y + 5 = 3(x + 1)$.

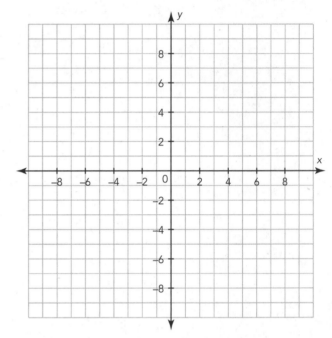

a. Determine a point on the graph of the equation.

b. Use the slope to determine another point on the line. Write the coordinates of the point.

c. Draw a line to graph the equation.

Name _____ Date _____

C. Use the two-intercepts method to graph each equation.

1. Graph the equation $5x + 6y = 30$.

2. Graph the equation $-5x + 3y = -15$.

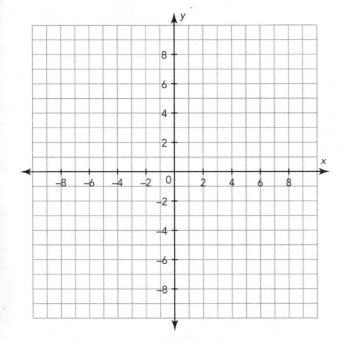

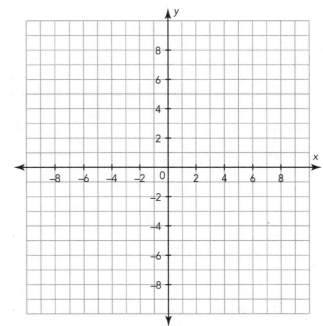

a. Determine the x-intercept by substituting 0 for y.

b. Determine the y-intercept by substituting 0 for x.

c. Draw a line to graph the equation.

a. Determine the x-intercept by substituting 0 for y.

b. Determine the y-intercept by substituting 0 for x.

c. Draw a line to graph the equation.

3. Graph the equation $3x + 5y = 30$.

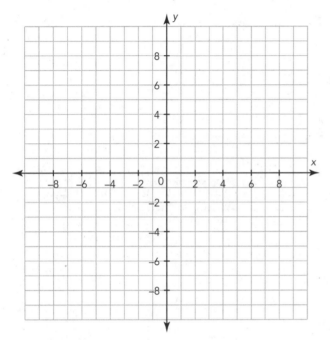

a. Determine the *x*-intercept by substituting 0 for *y*.

b. Determine the *y*-intercept by substituting 0 for *x*.

c. Draw a line to graph the equation.

4. Graph the equation $-4x - 5y = 40$.

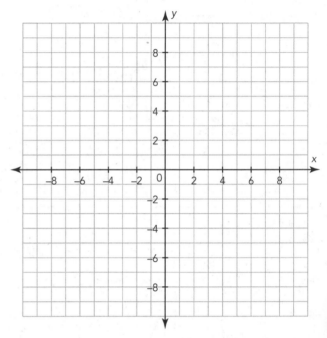

a. Determine the *x*-intercept by substituting 0 for *y*.

b. Determine the *y*-intercept by substituting 0 for *x*.

c. Draw a line to graph the equation.

Name _____ Date _____

5. Graph the equation $7x - 4y = -28$.

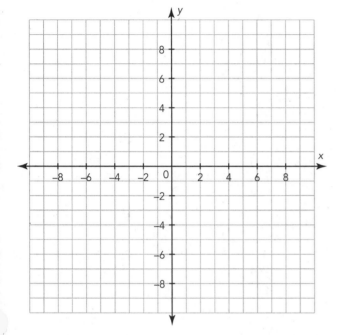

6. Graph the equation $-3x - 9y = -18$.

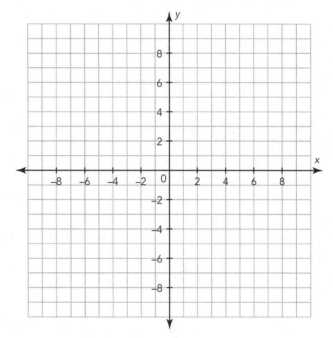

a. Determine the *x*-intercept by substituting 0 for *y*.

b. Determine the *y*-intercept by substituting 0 for *x*.

c. Draw a line to graph the equation.

a. Determine the *x*-intercept by substituting 0 for *y*.

b. Determine the *y*-intercept by substituting 0 for *x*.

c. Draw a line to graph the equation.

7. Graph the equation $-3x - 6y = 24$.

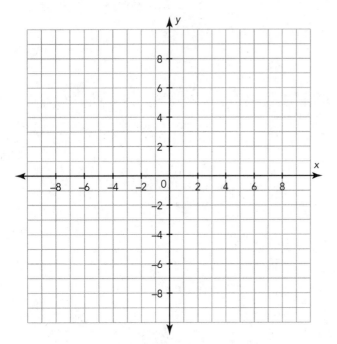

a. Determine the x-intercept by substituting 0 for y.

b. Determine the y-intercept by substituting 0 for x.

c. Draw a line to graph the equation.

8. Graph the equation $-9x + 9y = 54$.

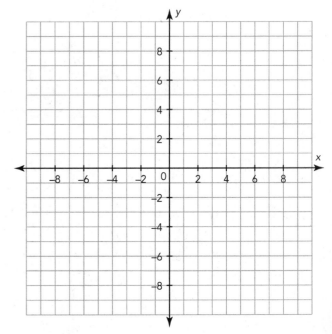

a. Determine the x-intercept by substituting 0 for y.

b. Determine the y-intercept by substituting 0 for x.

c. Draw a line to graph the equation.

Name _____   Date _____

9. Graph the equation $12x - 10y = 60$.

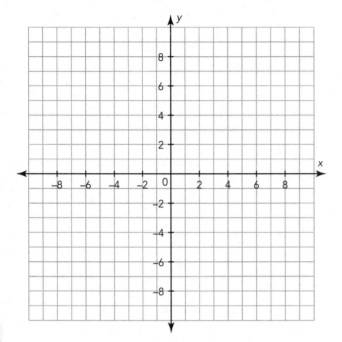

a. Determine the *x*-intercept by substituting 0 for *y*.

b. Determine the *y*-intercept by substituting 0 for *x*.

c. Draw a line to graph the equation.

10. Graph the equation $x - 3y = -9$.

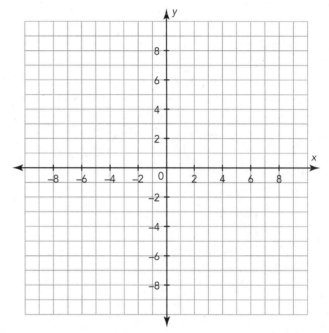

a. Determine the *x*-intercept by substituting 0 for *y*.

b. Determine the *y*-intercept by substituting 0 for *x*.

c. Draw a line to graph the equation.

11. Graph the equation $2x + 7y = -14$.

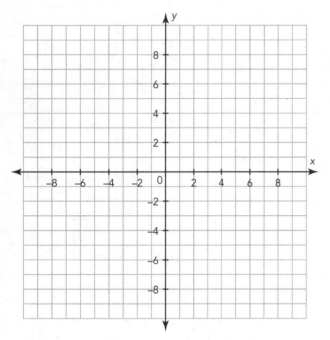

a. Determine the x-intercept by substituting 0 for y.

b. Determine the y-intercept by substituting 0 for x.

c. Draw a line to graph the equation.

12. Graph the equation $5x - y = 10$.

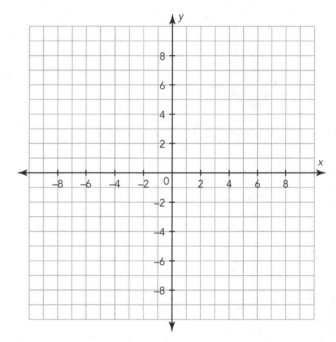

a. Determine the x-intercept by substituting 0 for y.

b. Determine the y-intercept by substituting 0 for x.

c. Draw a line to graph the equation.

Name _____ Date _____

IV. Writing Equations to Model Linear Relationships

A. Use the given information to determine each equation.

1. Point *D* is located at (−13, −1). Point *Q* is located at (0, 12). Determine the slope-intercept equation of line *DQ*.

2. Point *S* is located at (−9, 8). Point *G* is located at (−3, 3). Determine the slope-intercept equation of line *SG*.

3. Point *Q* is located at (−8, −10). Point *B* is located at (−3, −4). Determine the slope-intercept equation of line *QB*.

4. The slope of line *FL* is $\frac{3}{2}$. The *y*-intercept of line *FL* is (0, −6). Determine the standard form equation of line *FL*.

5. Point *V* is located at (−2, 7). Point *T* is located at (10, −8). Determine the slope-intercept equation of line *VT*.

6. Point *E* is located at (−5, −4). Point *C* is located at (1, 2). Determine the slope-intercept equation of line *EC*.

7. Point *R* is located at (−2, 5). Point *S* is located at (4, −2). Determine the slope-intercept equation of line *RS*.

8. The slope of line *AB* is −0.2. The *y*-intercept of line *AB* is (0, 2). Determine the standard form equation of line *AB*.

9. Point *W* is located at (−13, −13). Point *T* is located at (−7, −6). Determine the slope-intercept equation of line *WT*.

10. Point *Z* is located at (−10, −6). Point *D* is located at (5, 11). Determine the slope-intercept equation of line *ZD*.

11. Point *M* is located at (5, 1). Point *N* is located at (13, 12). Determine the slope-intercept equation of line *MN*.

12. The slope of line *OP* is 9. The *y*-intercept of line *OP* is (0, −3). Determine the standard form equation of line *OP*.

V. Modeling Linear Functions Using Multiple Representations

A. Solve each problem.

1. Kenya spent a total of 12 hours installing flooring in the dining room, and then more hours pulling it back up because it was so squeaky. Her total work time was divided evenly over 10 days.

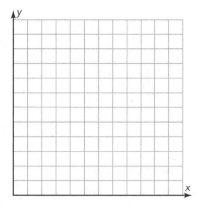

  a. Define variables for the time Kenya spent pulling up flooring and the time Kenya worked each day. Then write an equation to represent a relationship between the two quantities.

  b. Graph the equation.

  c. How many hours a day did she work on this project, if she spent 4 hours pulling up flooring?

2. Ms. Kindsey had each student bring a set of watercolors for art class. Each set had 2 brushes in it.

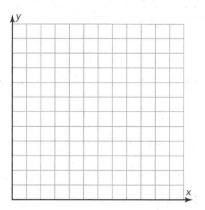

  a. Define variables for the number of students and the number of brushes. Then write an equation to represent a relationship between the two quantities.

  b. Graph the equation.

  c. How many brushes did Ms. Kindsey collect from thirteen students?

Name _____ Date _____

3. At the beginning of the summer, there are eleven rabbits living in a field. Each week for the rest of the summer, another rabbit moves in.

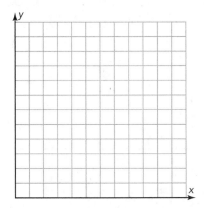

a. Define variables for the number of rabbits and the time in weeks. Then write an equation to represent a relationship between the two quantities.

b. Graph the equation.

c. When there are fifteen rabbits living in the field, how many weeks has it been?

4. You are in a harness preparing to explore a subterranean cave. As you begin, you are 4 feet above ground level. You then begin to descend. Your elevation changes at the rate of –1 foot per second. Treat elevations above ground level as positive and elevations below ground level as negative.

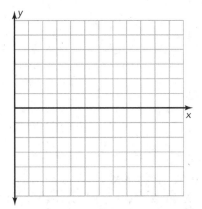

a. Define variables for the elevation in feet and the time in seconds. Then write an equation to represent a relationship between the two quantities.

b. Graph the equation.

c. What will your elevation be after 10 seconds?

5. The lights in the hallway at school are burning out at a rate of one per week. Each time an old light burns out, it gets replaced with an energy efficient LED bulb. At the start of the school year, there were only 7 LED bulbs in the hallway.

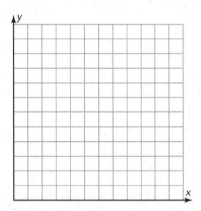

   a. Define variables for the number of LED bulbs and the time in weeks. Then write an equation to represent a relationship between the two quantities.

   b. Graph the equation.

   c. At the end of thirty weeks of school, how many LED bulbs were in the hallway?

6. Corinne is sponsoring a school dance to raise money to donate to charity. The charge for the room rental is $250. Corinne expects to raise $100 per week in donations. She will pay for the room rental from the donations.

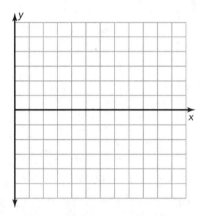

   a. Define variables for the amount Corinne has to donate to charity and the number of weeks. Then write an equation to represent a relationship between the two quantities.

   b. Graph the equation.

   c. How much money will Corinne have to donate to charity after 5 weeks of fundraising?

Name _____ Date _____

7. You bought 6 pounds of oranges from your local farmer's market.

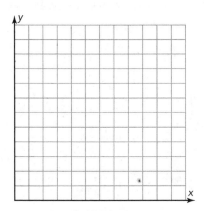

a. Define variables for the price in dollars per pound and the amount spent. Then write an equation to represent a relationship between the two quantities.

b. Graph the equation.

c. If you spent $8.40, what was the price per pound?

8. Max is in charge of all the baseball leagues in his town. He is assessing the different players in the leagues based on their ability to play different positions. He estimates that about 1 out of every 10 players in each league can play first base.

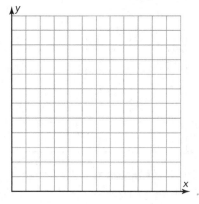

a. Define variables for the number of players who can play first base and the number of players in the league. Then write an equation to represent a relationship between the two quantities.

b. Graph the equation.

c. There are 520 players in the Rookie League. About how many players should be able to play first base from this league?

9. Courtney needs blue and brown ribbon to use to make a bow for a dress. According to her pattern she needs 11.2 inches of brown ribbon.

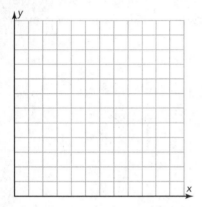

   a. Define variables for the total amount of inches of ribbon and the amount in inches of blue ribbon. Then write an equation to represent a relationship between the two quantities.

   b. Graph the equation.

   c. Courtney decides to increase the amount of ribbon to 19.5 inches. How much blue ribbon will Courtney use?

10. Noah looked as his household budget and determined that 1 out of every 8 dollars he spent on groceries were spent on snacks.

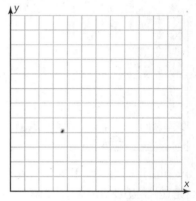

   a. Define variables for the amount in dollars spent on snacks and the amount in dollars spent on groceries. Then write an equation to represent a relationship between the two quantities.

   b. Graph the equation.

   c. If Noah spent $192 on groceries, how many dollars did he spend on snacks?

Name _____   Date _____

11. Three friends have applied for a loan to open a new business. A bank will loan them 1.2 million dollars. The three friends estimate that their business will make a profit of $0.6 million per year.

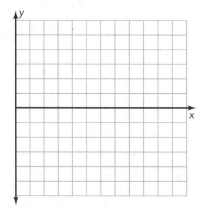

   a. Define variables for the financial status of the business in millions of dollars and the time since the company began. Then write an equation to represent a relationship between the two quantities.

   b. Graph the equation.

   c. If the estimates were correct, how long was it before the business was debt-free?

12. A website provides an average customer rating for each company on their site using a scale from −10 points to 10 points. The first average customer rating a new online company received was −7.0. As the company improves, the average customer rating increases at a rate of 1.5 points per week.

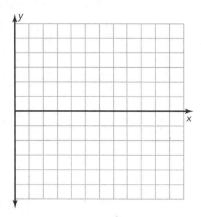

   a. Define variables for the average rating and the time in weeks. Then write an equation to represent a relationship between the two quantities.

   b. Graph the equation.

   c. How many weeks will it take for the company's average customer rating to be 1.5 points?

Introduction to Functions

Name _____ Date _____

I. Exploring Functions and Graphs of Functions

A. Determine the equation for the function shown in each table or graph.

1.

x	y
1	32
2.5	35
3	36
4	38

2.

x	y
2	−4
4	−6
7	−9
8	−10

3.

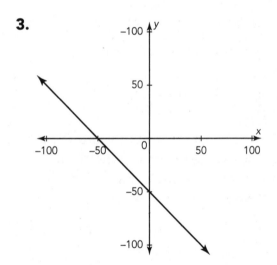

4.

x	y
$\frac{1}{3}$	21
1	23
$\frac{8}{3}$	28
4	32

5.

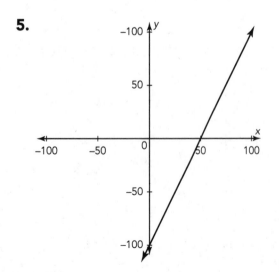

6.

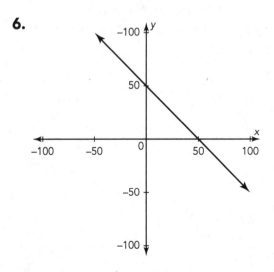

Name _____ Date _____

7.

x	y
2	2
5	$\frac{1}{2}$
6	0
9	$-1\frac{1}{2}$

8.

x	y
−2	−19
0	−17
3.5	−13.5
10	−7

9.

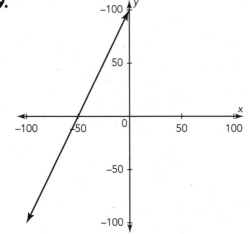

10.

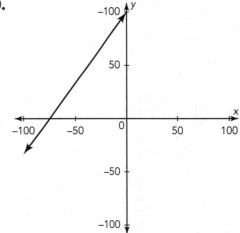

11.

x	y
−3	15
−1	11
9	−9
10	−11

12.

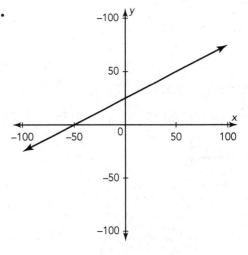

13.

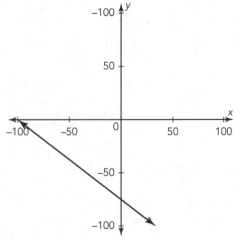

14.

x	y
0	-1
5	$-1\frac{1}{2}$
10	-2
40	-5

15.

x	y
-5	5
-1.5	19
1	29
2	33

16.

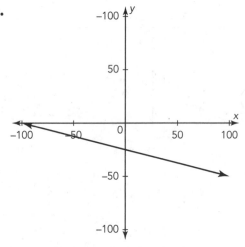

II. Classifying Relations and Functions

A. Write the corresponding ordered pairs and tell whether each relation is a function.

1.

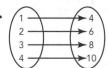

2.

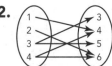

Name _____ Date _____

3.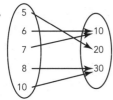

4.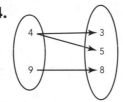

5.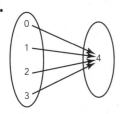

6.

Input	Output
4	5
8	12
12	16
16	20
20	24

7.

Input	Output
15	0
10	5
5	10
10	15
15	20

8.

x	y
0	15
5	10
10	5
15	10
20	15

9.

x	y
5	0
5	1
5	2
5	3
5	4

10.

x	y
−3	9
−1	1
0	0
1	1
3	9

B. Determine whether each given situation represents a function. Explain your answer.

1. *Input*: Lila mails 6 different valentines to her friends.
   Output: Each of Lila's 6 friends receives a valentine from her.

2. *Input*: There is 1 copy of a popular book in the library.
   Output: The book has been checked out by 45 different people.

3. *Input*: The principal of a school sends the same memo to all of the teachers.
   Output: There are 28 teachers in the school.

4. *Input*: There are 13 cats for adoption at the animal shelter.
   Output: Each cat is adopted by a different family.

5. *Input*: There are 3 showings of a play.
   Output: Over 200 people attend each showing.

6. *Input*: Garrett bakes 2 dozen cookies for the bake sale.
   Output: Twenty-four people buy a cookie.

7. *Input*: The new issue of Sports Today is published.
   Output: Issues are sent to millions of readers.

8. *Input*: Yi Ling has French on Mondays, Wednesdays, and Fridays, and German on Tuesdays and Thursdays.
   Output: Yi Ling's language classes per day.

9. *Input*: There is a flight from Los Angeles to New York.
   Output: There are 350 passengers on the flight.

10. *Input*: There are five different trails in a park.
   Output: Three friends take one of the trails.

Name _____ Date _____

C. Determine whether each graph represents a function.

1.
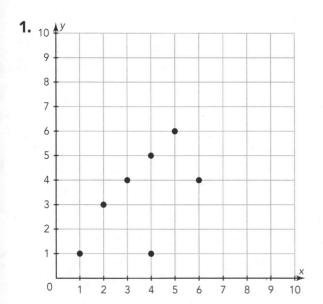

2.
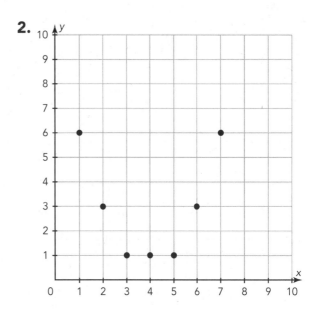

3.
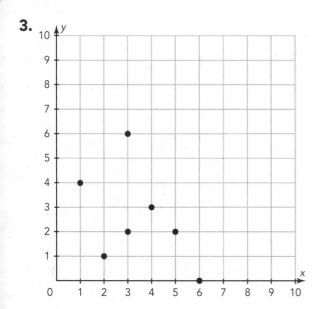

4.
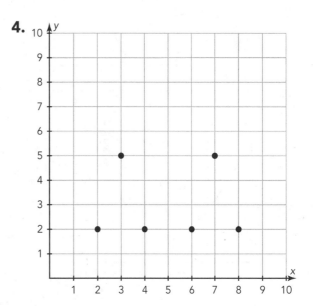

5.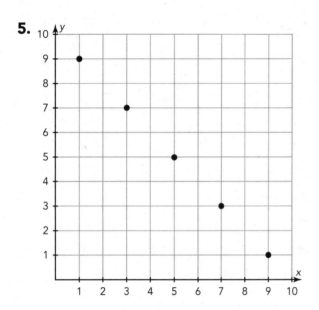

6.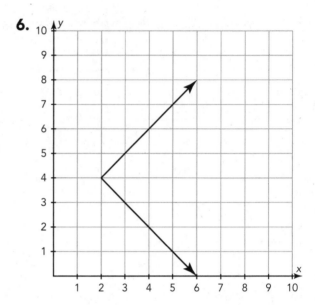

7.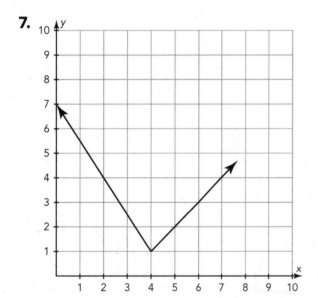

8.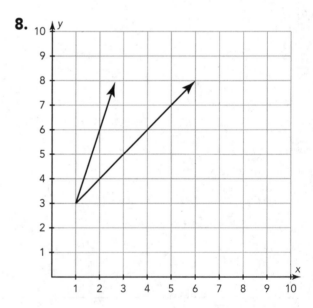

Name _____ Date _____

9.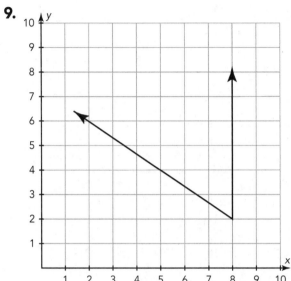

10.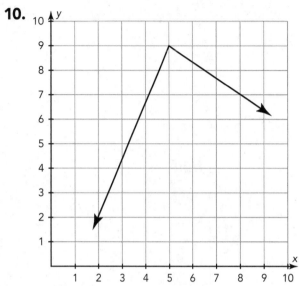

D. Determine whether each equation is a function. If it is not a function, explain why not.

1. $y = 3x + 1$

2. $y = x^2$

3. $y^2 = x$

4. $y = \sqrt{x + 5}$

5. $y = -|x|$

6. $\sqrt{y} = x - 8$

7. $y = \frac{1}{2}x$

8. $|y| = 6 + 4x$

9. $y = x^3$

10. $x = 1$

III. Identifying Key Characteristics of Graphs from Functions

A. Answer the questions about each given graph.

1.

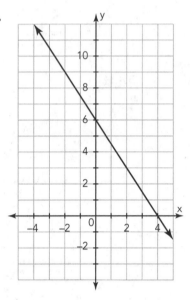

a. What is the x-intercept?

b. What is the y-intercept?

c. What is the domain?

d. What is the range?

e. Is the slope positive, negative, or 0?

2.

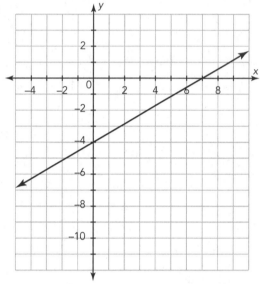

a. What is the x-intercept?

b. What is the y-intercept?

c. What is the domain?

d. What is the range?

e. Is the slope positive, negative, or 0?

Name _____   Date _____

3.

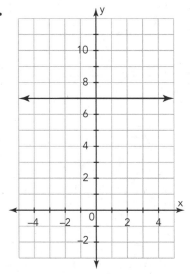

a. What is the x-intercept?

b. What is the y-intercept?

c. What is the domain?

d. What is the range?

e. Is the slope positive, negative, or 0?

4.

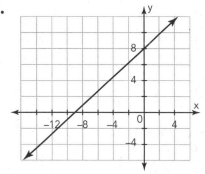

a. What is the x-intercept?

b. What is the y-intercept?

c. What is the domain?

d. What is the range?

e. Is the slope positive, negative, or 0?

5.

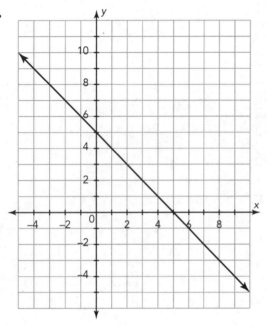

a. What is the x-intercept?

b. What is the y-intercept?

c. What is the domain?

d. What is the range?

e. Is the slope positive, negative, or 0?

6.

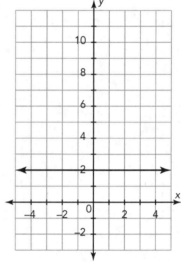

a. What is the x-intercept?

b. What is the y-intercept?

c. What is the domain?

d. What is the range?

e. Is the slope positive, negative, or 0?

Name _____   Date _____

7.

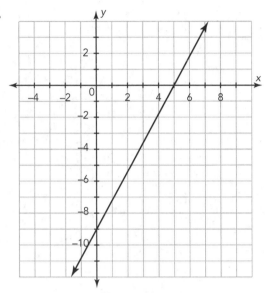

a. What is the x-intercept?

b. What is the y-intercept?

c. What is the domain?

d. What is the range?

e. Is the slope positive, negative, or 0?

8.

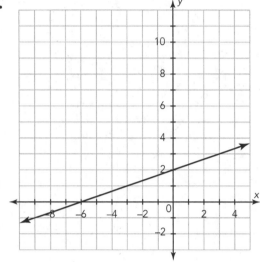

a. What is the x-intercept?

b. What is the y-intercept?

c. What is the domain?

d. What is the range?

e. Is the slope positive, negative, or 0?

9.

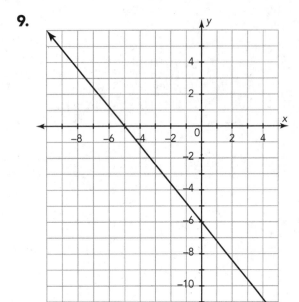

a. What is the x-intercept?

b. What is the y-intercept?

c. What is the domain?

d. What is the range?

e. Is the slope positive, negative, or 0?

10.

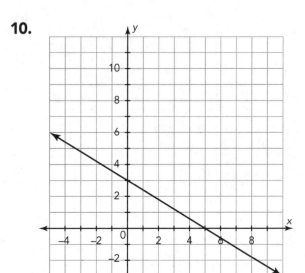

a. What is the x-intercept?

b. What is the y-intercept?

c. What is the domain?

d. What is the range?

e. Is the slope positive, negative, or 0?

Name _____   Date _____

11.

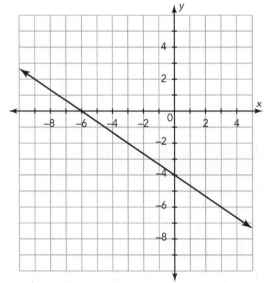

a. What is the x-intercept?

b. What is the y-intercept?

c. What is the domain?

d. What is the range?

e. Is the slope positive, negative, or 0?

12.

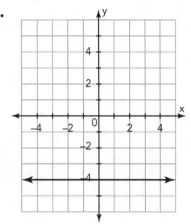

a. What is the x-intercept?

b. What is the y-intercept?

c. What is the domain?

d. What is the range?

e. Is the slope positive, negative, or 0?

Topic 4
Patterns in Bivariate Data

Name _____ Date _____

I. Estimating Lines of Best Fit

A. Tell whether each graph shows a positive linear association, a negative linear association, a non-linear association, or no association.

1.

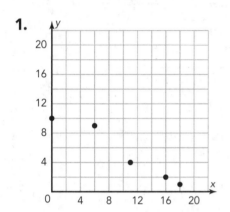

2.

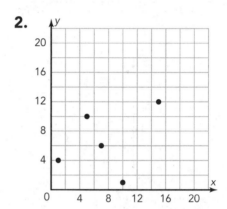

3.

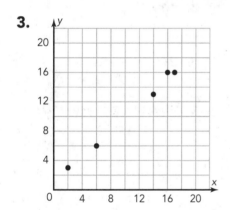

4.

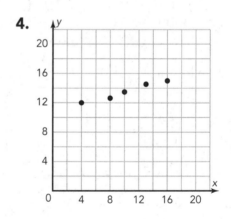

5.

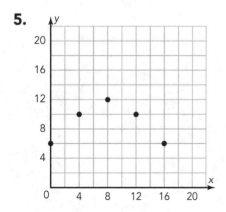

6.

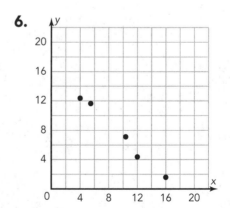

Name _____ Date _____

7.

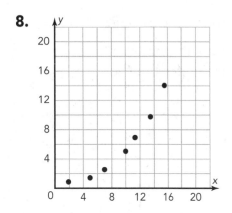

8.

9.

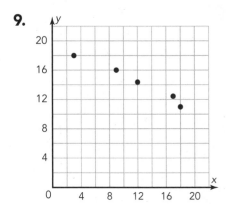

10.

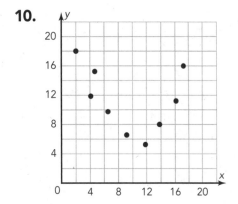

11.

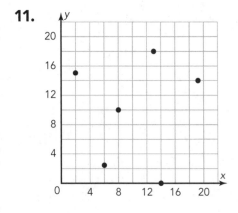

12.

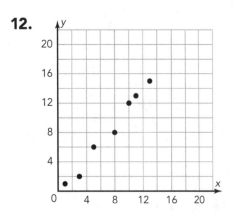

II. Using Lines of Best Fit

A. Use two points to estimate the slope and y-intercept of the line of best fit. Then, write the equation that estimates the line.

1.

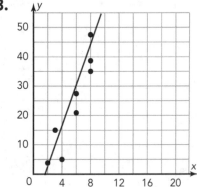

Slope:

y-intercept:

Line of best fit equation:

2.

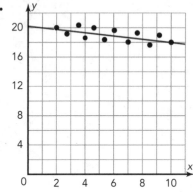

Slope:

y-intercept:

Line of best fit equation:

3.

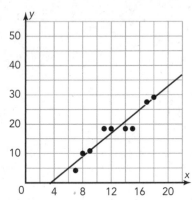

Slope:

y-intercept:

Line of best fit equation:

4.

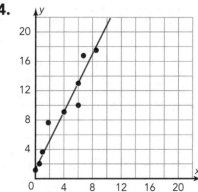

Slope:

y-intercept:

Line of best fit equation:

Name _____ Date _____

5.

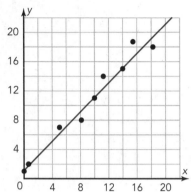

Slope:

y-intercept:

Line of best fit equation:

6.

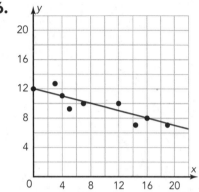

Slope:

y-intercept:

Line of best fit equation:

7.

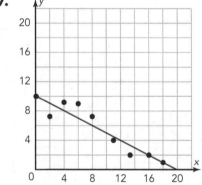

Slope:

y-intercept:

Line of best fit equation:

8.

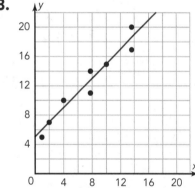

Slope:

y-intercept:

Line of best fit equation:

9.

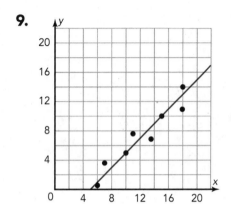

Slope:

y-intercept:

Line of best fit equation:

10.

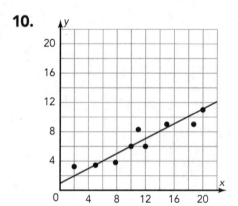

Slope:

y-intercept:

Line of best fit equation:

11.

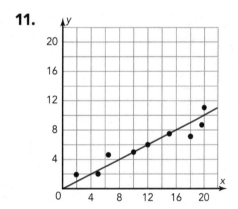

Slope:

y-intercept:

Line of best fit equation:

12.

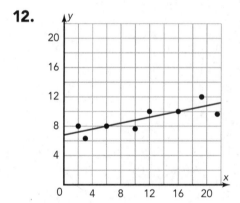

Slope:

y-intercept:

Line of best fit equation:

Name Adriana Ramirez   Date 2/28/22

B. Use the given equation to answer each question.

1. A grocery store's earnings in dollars can be modeled by the equation $y = 0.75x - 0.15x$, where x represents the number of tomatoes that they sell. If they sell 200 tomatoes in one day, how much money do they earn?

$200 = 0.75x - 0.15x$

$\dfrac{200}{0.6x} = \dfrac{0.6x}{0.6x}$

$\boxed{x = 199.4}$ $

2. The number of T-shirts that a T-shirt company sells can be modeled by the equation $y = 218x + 520$, where the price of a T-shirt is represented by x. If they sell their T-shirts for $8 each, how many will they sell?

3. The distance a car can travel in miles is modeled by the equation $y = 23x - 6$, where x represents the number of gallons of gas the car uses. If the car traveled 86 miles, how many gallons of gas did it use?

4. The amount a shoe store charges in dollars to deliver x pairs of shoes can be modeled by the equation $y = 40x + 30$. If the total bill was $350 dollars, how many pairs of shoes did they deliver?

5. The number of gallons of water, y, in a swimming pool is modeled by the equation $y = 7.5x + 500$, where x represents the time in minutes after the pump is turned on. How many gallons of water are in the pool if the pump runs for 200 minutes?

6. The height of a tree in feet, y, is modeled by the equation $y = 2.5x + 3$, where x represents the age of the tree in years. How old will the tree be when it is 33 feet tall?

Topic 1
Solving Linear Equations

Name _____ Date _____

I. Exploring Two-Step Equations

A. Use the balance tool to help you solve each equation.

1. $2q + 4 = 6$

2. $6 = 3p + 3$

3. $3a + 1 = 5 + 5$

4. $4 + 5 = 4m + 1$

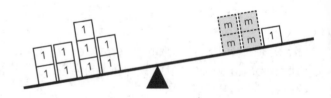

5. $5 + 2 = 2b + 3$

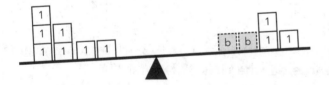

6. $2w + 6 = 2 + 4$

Name _____ Date _____

B. Use inverse operations to isolate the variable and solve each equation.

1. $5x + 15 = 75$ **2.** $4x - 3 = 37$

3. $\frac{t}{3} + 14 = 29$ **4.** $\frac{3}{4}x + 2 = 4\frac{2}{3}$

5. $-\frac{n}{5} - 9 = 21$ **6.** $2 = 2.27 - \frac{m}{4}$

C. Match each equation to an equivalent equation solved for x.

1. $\frac{1}{2}x + 1 = 9$ **a.** $x = \frac{9 - 1}{2}$

2. $-\frac{1}{3}x - 2 = 6$ **b.** $x = \frac{9 + 1}{2}$

3. $3x - 2 = 6$ **c.** $x = 2(9 - 1)$

4. $2x - 1 = 9$ **d.** $x = 2(9 + 1)$

5. $\frac{1}{3}x - 2 = 6$ **e.** $x = \frac{6 + 2}{-3}$

6. $\frac{1}{2}x - 1 = 9$ **f.** $x = \frac{6 + 2}{3}$

7. $2x + 1 = 9$ **g.** $x = 3(6 + 2)$

8. $-3x - 2 = 6$ **h.** $x = -3(6 + 2)$

II. Solving Multi-Step Equations

A. Solve for x.

1. $7 + 4x = 63 - 10x$ **2.** $9x - 9 = 10x - 7$

3. $9 + 4x = -10x - 5$ **4.** $10 + x = -9x + 2$

5. $3 + 4x = -3 + 6x$ **6.** $7x - 9 = 3x - 29$

7. $5x - 3 = 3 + 2x$ **8.** $-4x + 6 = 9x - 8$

9. $-10x + 2 = -3 + 8x$ **10.** $47 + 10x = -10x + 7$

11. $5x + 1 = -3 + 10x$ **12.** $24 - 4x = 2x$

III. Solving Equations with One Solution, Infinite, and No Solutions

A. Determine whether each equation has one solution, no solutions, or infinite solutions.

1. $5 = 0$

2. $4 = y$

3. $10b = 10b$

4. $x = 5$

5. $8 = 2$

6. $x = x$

7. $9 = x - 4$

8. $x + 3 = x + 3$

9. $2x = 3x$

10. $x + 8 = x$

11. $x + 3 = 5$

12. $6z = (3 + 3)z$

13. $x - 2 = 2$

14. $9 - c = 2c$

15. $g - 0 = g + 1$

16. $0 = 0$

17. $3(f + 1) = 3f - 3$

18. $0 = p$

19. $x - 4 = x - 2 - 2$

20. $9f = f + 9$

21. $1a = 0$

22. $\frac{q}{q} = 1$

23. $\frac{9}{s} = 3\left(\frac{3}{s}\right)$

24. $20\left(\frac{y}{5}\right) - 7 = 4y + 3$

B. Solve each equation. Tell whether the equation has one solution, no solutions, or infinite solutions.

1. $10(x - 2) + 15 = 8x + 7$

2. $x + 6(x - 1) = 7(3 + x)$

3. $3(3x + 4) - 2x - 5 - 7x = 20$

4. $8x - 8 = 6x - 5 + 2(x - 1.5)$

5. $12x + 9 - 4x - 4 = 3x - 7 - x + 30$

6. $5 + 5x - 3 = 5x + 9$

7. $4x + 1 + 3x + 2 + 3x + 7 = 5(2x + 2)$

8. $\frac{4(x - 8)}{5} = 16$

9. $6x - 5 - 2x + 8 = 12\left(\frac{1}{3}x + \frac{1}{4}\right)$

10. $2(-7x + 5) + 2x = 3x + 3 - 15x$

11. $\frac{9}{x} + 2 = 20$

12. $-5x + 4(3 + 2.5x) = 8x + 12 - 3x$

Topic 2
Systems of Linear Equations

Name _____ Date _____

I. Modeling Linear Systems

A. Graph each system of linear equations. Use the graph to answer the questions.

1. Shawn started walking from home to school just as his brother Dante was leaving school to walk home. The distance from their home to school is 11,680 feet. Dante was walking at a slow pace averaging about 280 feet per minute. Shawn, who was excited to get to class, was walking more quickly, averaging about 450 feet per minute. Assume they both left at the same time and maintained their rate of speed for the entire trip.

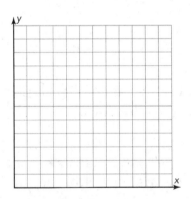

a. How far was each sibling from home after 6 minutes?

b. When was Dante 8320 feet from home?

c. How long after leaving did Shawn meet Dante?

2. Sylvia runs a company that produces clothing accessories—hats, patches, scarves, etc.—for events such as a Presidential inauguration. To produce each item costs her $1. She also pays an initial startup cost for production of $100, regardless of the number of products that she produces. She plans to sell each product for $5.

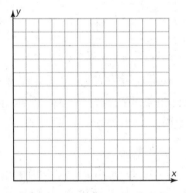

a. How much money would the cost be to produce fifty products? What is Sylvia's income if she sells fifty products?

b. If her income was $235, how many products did she sell?

c. How many products must Sylvia produce if she wants her income from this product to be equal to her production cost?

3. Computer Company A had total sales of 4.9 billion dollars in 2013. Its sales have been declining at the rate of 0.22 billion dollars per year. Computer Company B, another major manufacturer of computers, had total sales of 1.64 billion dollars in 2013. Its sales have been increasing at a rate of 0.19 billion dollars per year.

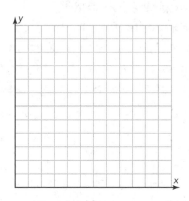

a. What will Computer Company A's and Computer Company B's predicted total sales be for the year 2022?

b. In how many years will Computer Company A's predicted total sales reach 4.24 billion dollars?

c. In how many years will the predicted sales for these two computer companies be equal?

4. Deep-sea divers Jacques Cousteau and his assistant are searching for sunken treasure. Jacques Cousteau is currently 13.9 meters below the surface (−13.9 meters) and his assistant is currently 97.3 meters below the surface (−97.3 meters). Jacques Cousteau is swimming down at the rate of 7.5 meters per minute, and his assistant is swimming towards the surface at 6.4 meters per minute.

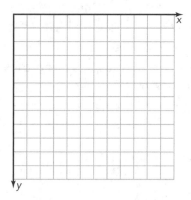

a. What is the depth of each diver 3 minutes from now?

b. In how many minutes will the assistant be 33.3 meters below the surface?

c. According to the algebraic model, in how many minutes will the divers be at the same depth?

Name _____   Date _____

5. Jean and Brian both have coffee cans in which they keep quarters. Jean has 64 quarters in her can while Brian has 228 in his. This summer Brian is working at the library five days per week and spends 3 of his quarters every day in the parking meter. Jean, however, receives 1 quarter every day in change from her lunch and is putting them into her can. (Jean also works five days per week.)

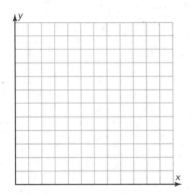

a. How many quarters will Jean and Brian have after 2 full work weeks?

b. At this rate, after how many business days will Brian's can be empty?

c. In how many business days will both cans have the same amount of money?

6. In a hot air balloon race, one balloon goes up and is given some time to get a head start. The other balloons are launched together to chase the first one. The winner is the first chase balloon that gets within a certain distance of the target balloon. Suppose the target balloon is launched and given a headstart of 4.7 miles, and travels at the rate of 0.2 miles per minute. Mr. Montgolfiere is chasing it. His balloon has a top speed of 0.3 miles per minute.

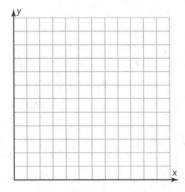

a. How far will Mr. Montgolfiere's balloon have traveled after 30 minutes?

b. When will the target balloon have traveled 13.7 miles?

c. At what time will Mr. Montgolfiere's balloon catch the target balloon?

7. In a 1994 survey, 1 in 2 respondents reported that they usually did not take protective measures for sun exposure. One person in 8 reported having been sunburned in the past year.

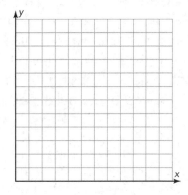

a. If these rates were true for a town of 320 people, how many people would be unlikely to protect themselves? How many would be likely to be sunburned?

b. If twenty people reported that they were sunburned last year, how many people were surveyed?

c. Would the number of people who were sunburned and the number of people who didn't protect themselves ever be equal? When?

8. It was estimated that the Pittsburgh metropolitan area would have a population of 2,377,800 people at the end of 1993. Its population was expected to increase at the rate of 10 people per day. The metropolitan area of Tampa Bay was estimated to have a population of 2,067,000 at the end of 1993. Its population was expected to increase at the rate of 130 people per day. Assume there are 365 days in a year.

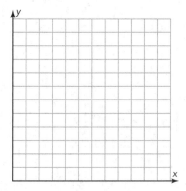

a. What was the population of Pittsburgh 3 years later, at the end of 1996?

b. According to the algebraic model, in how many days will the population of the Pittsburgh metropolitan area reach three million?

c. In how many days does the model predict that the populations of the two metropolitan areas were or will be equal?

Name _____ Date _____

9. Two skydivers are jumping out of two separate planes to do a stunt for a movie. The first skydiver is at an altitude of 2700 feet and will fall at the rate of 95 feet per second by stretching out his arms and legs to slow his descent. The second skydiver will jump from an altitude of 3600 feet but will fall at the rate of 185 feet per second.

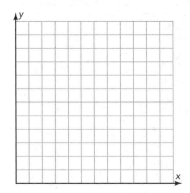

a. What will each skydiver's altitude be in thirteen seconds?

b. After how many seconds will the first skydiver's altitude be 2225 feet?

c. When will the two skydivers' altitudes be equal?

10. Under one current health insurance plan, you get different insurance coverage depending on whether or not you go to someone who is associated with the plan. If you go to a provider who is not a member of the health plan, the plan will cover only 65% of your medical bill after the first $225. You pay the rest. However, if you go to a doctor or health provider who is a plan member, the plan will cover 100% of your bill after the first $70.

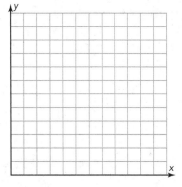

a. If you had $560 worth of doctor's bills, how much would be covered if you visited a member provider? a non-member provider?

b. If the health plan paid $510 when you went to a member provider, how much was your medical bill?

c. According to the algebraic model, is the coverage for member and non-member providers ever the same? If so, when, and can that cost ever occur in real life?

11. Yumi is planning a wedding shower for her best friend. She has come up with two options. The first option is to rent a hall and have the shower there. She figures the hall would cost $195 and food, refreshments, and decorations would cost $650. She also plans to give everyone some flowers in a vase. The vase would cost $4 and the flowers would cost $3.50. The second option is to take everyone on a river cruise. The Liberty Belle has a party package for $23.75 per person.

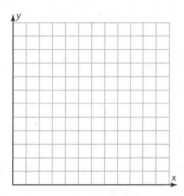

a. If 39 people attend the shower, how much will each option cost?

b. If Yumi has $1900 set aside for this function, how many people can she invite if she chooses option #2?

c. For what amount of people is the cost of both options the same?

12. Old growth forests are forests that have not experienced unnatural or man-made disturbances. Currently, the United States has about thirteen thousand square miles designated as old growth forest, and this is increasing at the rate of 340 square miles a year. The logging industry proposes that it be permitted to harvest 990 square miles of old growth timber per year.

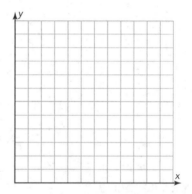

a. How many square miles of old growth forest will be harvested in the next 9 years if the timber industry gets the quotas they are requesting?

b. When will 9900 square miles be harvested?

c. When will the size of the old growth forest be equal to the amount harvested under the logging industry's proposal?

Name _____   Date _____

13. Ms. Williamson woke up one morning to find her basement flooded with water. She called two different plumbers to get their rates. The first plumber charges $36 just to walk in the door plus $28 an hour. The second plumber charges a flat $64 an hour.

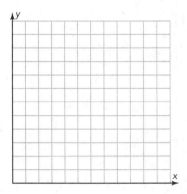

a. What is the cost for each plumber if the job takes four hours?

b. How many hours did the first plumber take to do the job if he charged $176?

c. After how many hours will the cost for both plumbers be the same?

14. A company was hired to build a tunnel through a mountain. The company started at the south end of the mountain and completed only 545 feet of the required 5450 feet before going bankrupt. A different company was hired to complete the job, but they decided to use two crews. Crew A would start where the other company left off at the southern end, while Crew B would start at the northern end and dig towards the other crew. Crew A was able to dig 22 feet of the tunnel per week. Crew B, which was larger, was able to dig 87 feet of the tunnel per week.

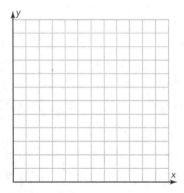

a. How far from the southern end are both crews after 25 weeks of digging?

b. When will Crew A be 853 feet from the southern opening?

c. How long after they start digging will they meet?

15. A couple of college students get the idea to open a snack stand at the regatta festival this summer. The students sell delicious soft pretzels. They pay the city $648 to set up their stand for the entire regatta. They also figure the cost for dough, coarse salt, and other things they need is $0.20 per pretzel. They sell each pretzel for $2.90.

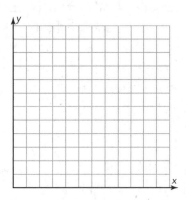

a. What is the cost and the income obtained from selling forty pretzels?

b. If the income from selling the pretzels was $261, how many pretzels did they sell?

c. How many pretzels must they sell to break even, according to the algebraic model?

16. A hot-air balloon rising at a rate of 52.2 feet per minute left the ground and, after some time, is now at an altitude of 425.4 feet. A blimp overhead at an altitude of 7231.8 feet begins descending at the rate of 160.5 feet per minute.

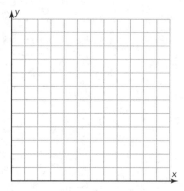

a. What is the height of the balloon and the blimp thirty-three minutes from now?

b. How long does the hot-air balloon take to reach a height of 1834.8 feet?

c. When will the balloon and the blimp be at the same height?

Name _____ Date _____

II. Solving Linear Systems

A. Graph the equations in each system. Tell whether the system has one solution, no solutions, or infinite solutions. If the system has one solution, write the values of the variables that make the equations true.

1. $\begin{cases} x = 2.25 \\ y = 4x - 3 \end{cases}$

2. $\begin{cases} y = -10 \\ y = 2x + 7 \end{cases}$

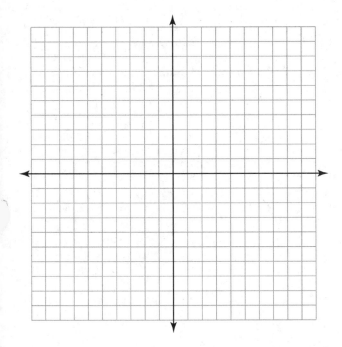

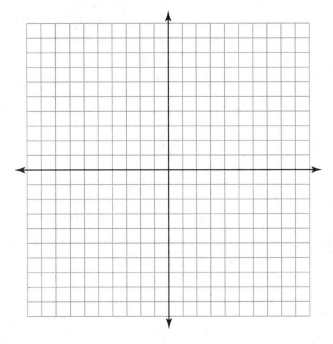

3. $\begin{cases} 4x - 2y = 12 \\ y = 2x - 6 \end{cases}$

4. $\begin{cases} -12x + 6y = -6 \\ y = -3x - 11 \end{cases}$

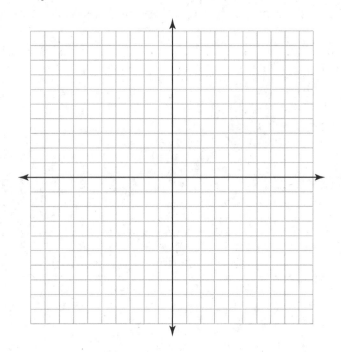

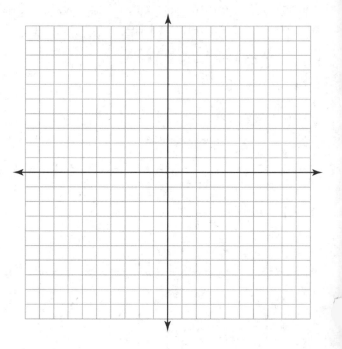

Name _____ Date _____

5. $\begin{cases} y = 4x - 30 \\ y = -3x + 5 \end{cases}$

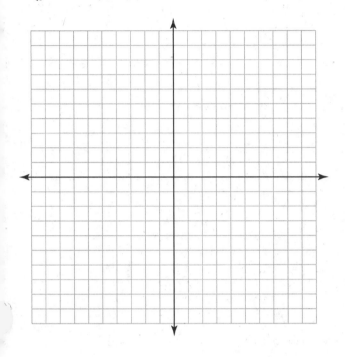

6. $\begin{cases} -5x + 10y = -10 \\ x = 2y + 4 \end{cases}$

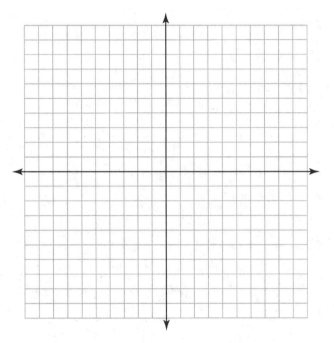

7. $\begin{cases} y = 3x + 17 \\ 10x + 5y = -15 \end{cases}$

8. $\begin{cases} -8x - 8y = -10 \\ x = 3.25 \end{cases}$

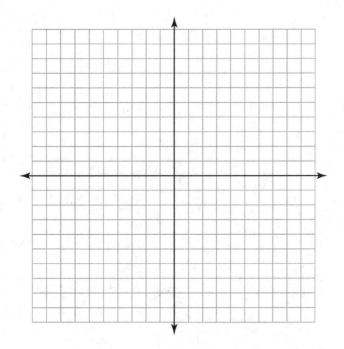

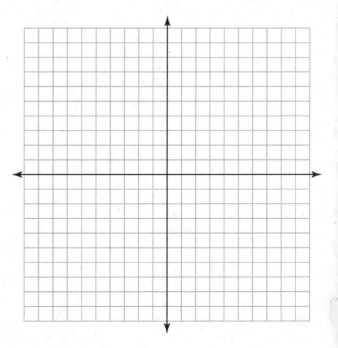

Name _____ Date _____

9. $\begin{cases} -1.5x + 0.5y = -2 \\ y = 3x - 4 \end{cases}$

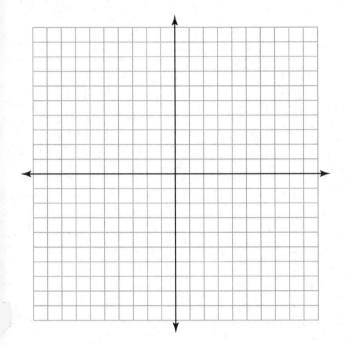

10. $\begin{cases} y = 3 \\ y = 2x - 13 \end{cases}$

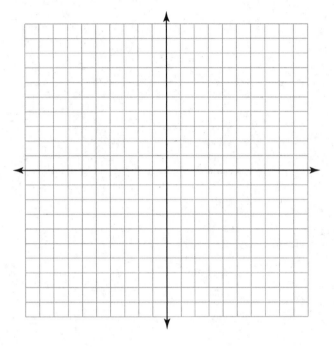

11. $\begin{cases} 2x - y = -15 \\ x = -8 \end{cases}$

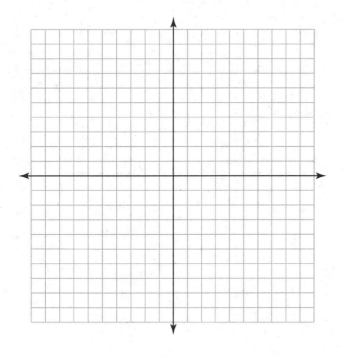

12. $\begin{cases} x = 7 - y \\ 2y + 2x = -6 \end{cases}$

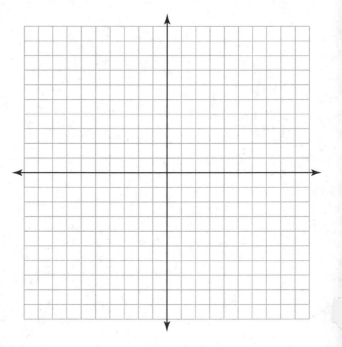

Name _____ Date _____

13. $\begin{cases} 3x + y = -6 \\ y = -2x - 4 \end{cases}$

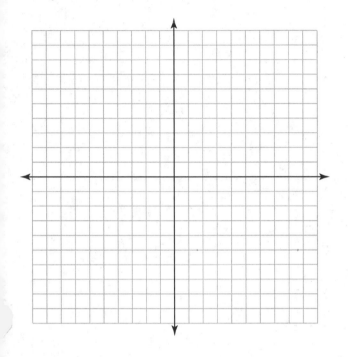

14. $\begin{cases} -x + y = 3 \\ y = -4x + 18 \end{cases}$

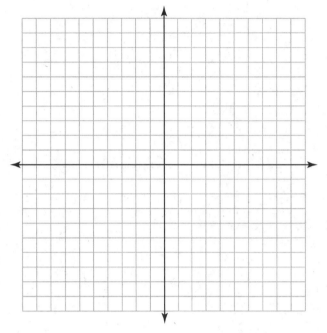

15. $18x - 3y = -15$
$y = 6x + 5$

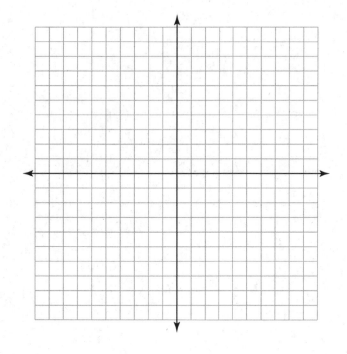

16. $y = 4$
$y = 3x + 16$

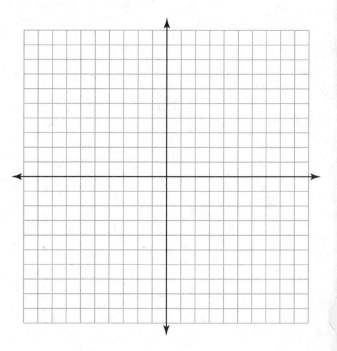

Topic 1
The Real Number System

Name _____ Date _____

I. Introduction to Irrational Numbers

A. Determine whether each number is a perfect square. If it is a perfect square, write the number as a product of its two factors.

1. 20   **2.** 36

3. 49   **4.** 68

5. 121   **6.** 169

7. 400   **8.** 150

B. Determine the square root for each perfect square.

1. $\sqrt{64}$ **2.** $\sqrt{100}$

3. $\sqrt{81}$ **4.** $\sqrt{16}$

5. $\sqrt{4}$ **6.** $\sqrt{0}$

7. $\sqrt{25}$ **8.** $\sqrt{144}$

C. Approximate each square root to the nearest tenth.

1. $\sqrt{130}$ **2.** $\sqrt{8}$

3. $\sqrt{85}$ **4.** $\sqrt{40}$

5. $\sqrt{24}$ **6.** $\sqrt{110}$

D. Classify each number as rational or irrational.

1. 0   **2.** −5

3. $-\sqrt{2}$ **4.** 1.3

5. $\sqrt{5}$ **6.** π

7. 0.33   **8.** $\sqrt{16}$

9. 6   **10.** $\frac{3}{4}$

11. 0.67236982158...   **12.** $\frac{31}{13}$

II. Graphing Real Numbers on a Number Line

A. Plot a point on the number line to represent each given number.

1. Represent −2.257 on the number line.

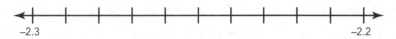

2. Represent $7\frac{1}{9}$ on the number line.

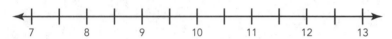

3. Represent $-\sqrt{4}$ on the number line.

4. Represent π on the number line.

5. Represent $4\frac{7}{8}$ on the number line.

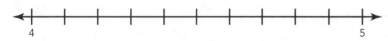

6. Represent $-\sqrt{28}$ on the number line.

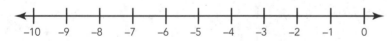

Name _____ Date _____

III. Ordering Rational and Irrational Numbers

A. Plot points to represent the given numbers on each number line. Then, order the numbers from least to greatest.

1. 92%, π, $-\sqrt{2}$, $-3\frac{8}{9}$

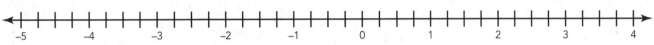

2. $-4\frac{1}{2}$, $\sqrt{16}$, 235%, π

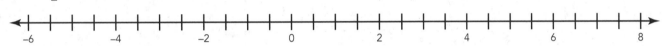

3. 143%, $\sqrt{4}$, π, 2.7

4. π, $7\frac{3}{4}$, 10%, 107%

5. π, $\sqrt{2}$, 5.67, $\frac{5}{8}$

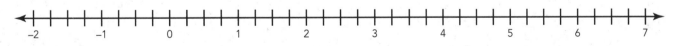

6. 375%, $-\sqrt{25}$, $-\sqrt{74}$, 7.589

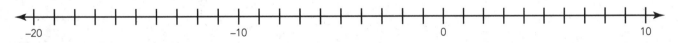

Topic 2
The Pythagorean Theorem

Name __Adriana Ramirez__ Date __1/11/21__

I. Applying the Pythagorean Theorem

A. Use the Pythagorean Theorem to determine each unknown measure.

1.

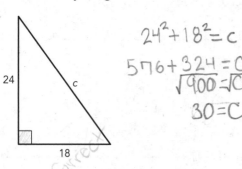

$$24^2 + 18^2 = c$$
$$576 + 324 = c$$
$$\sqrt{900} = \sqrt{c}$$
$$30 = c$$

Correct

2.

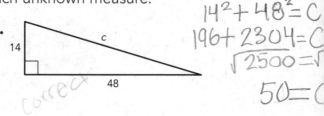

$$14^2 + 48^2 = c$$
$$196 + 2304 = c$$
$$\sqrt{2500} = \sqrt{}$$
$$50 = c$$

Correct

3.

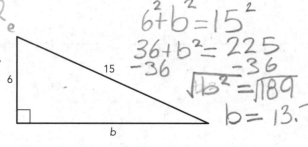

$$6^2 + b^2 = 15^2$$
$$36 + b^2 = 225$$
$$-36 \qquad -36$$
$$\sqrt{b^2} = \sqrt{189}$$
$$b = 13.7$$

4.

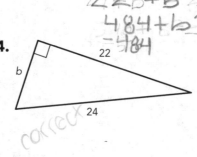

$$22^2 + b^2 = 24^2$$
$$484 + b^2 = 576$$
$$-484 \qquad -484$$
$$-576$$

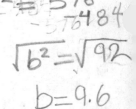

$$\sqrt{b^2} = \sqrt{92}$$
$$b = 9.6$$

Correct

5.

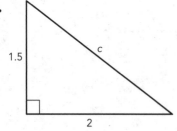

6.

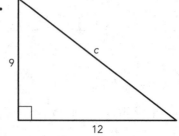

Name _____ Date _____

7.

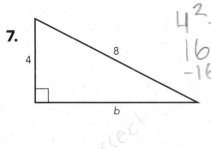

$4^2 + b^2 = 8^2$
$16 + b^2 = 64$
$-16 \qquad -16$
$\sqrt{b^2} = \sqrt{48}$
$b = 6.9$

Correct

8.

$5^2 + 7^2 = C^2$
$25 + 49 = C^2$
$\sqrt{74} = C$
$8.60 = C$

Correct

9.

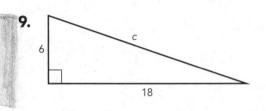

10.

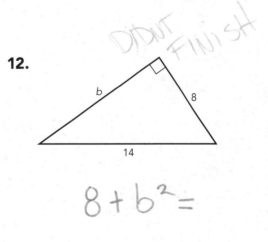

DIDNT FINISH

11.

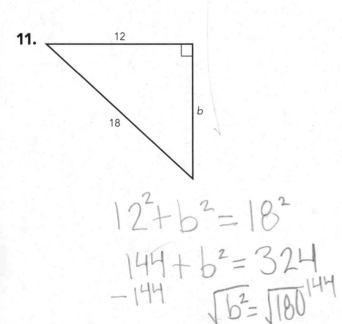

$12^2 + b^2 = 18^2$
$144 + b^2 = 324$
$-144 \qquad -144$
$\sqrt{b^2} = \sqrt{180}$
$b \approx 13.4$

12.

$8 + b^2 =$

$b \approx 11.5$

II. Problem Solving Using the Pythagorean Theorem

A. Solve each problem.

1. A carpenter needs to do some repairs to the top of a 24-foot wall. He wants the tip of the ladder to rest on the top of the wall. How far must he place his 26-foot ladder from the base of the wall?

2. An airplane is flying directly over your house. The distance between your house and the airport is 12 miles. The altitude of the airplane is 4 miles. Determine the distance between the airplane and the airport to the nearest hundredth of a mile.

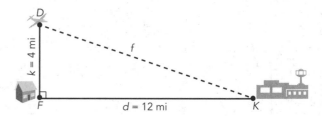

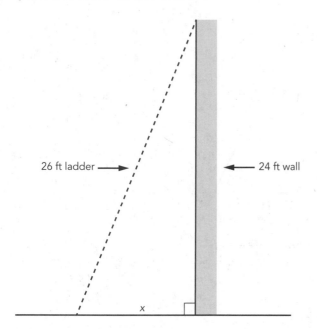

Name _____   Date _____

3. You are mountain climbing. You see a cliff directly in front of you. The distance from your feet to the base of the cliff is 23 feet, and the distance from your feet to the top of the cliff is 26 feet. Determine the height of the cliff to the nearest hundredth of a foot.

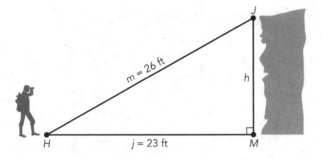

4. You are helping your friend move furniture. You need to know the width, height, and diagonal of the front door frame. The width of the door frame is 36 inches, and the length of the diagonal of the door frame is 96 inches. What is the height of the door frame to the nearest inch?

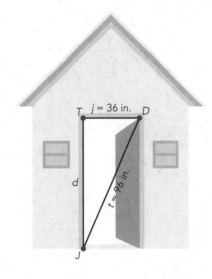

5. You are standing in front of a flagpole. The distance from your feet to the base of the pole is 17 feet, and the height of the pole is 9 feet. Determine the distance from your feet to the top of the pole to the nearest hundredth of a foot.

6. You are building an entertainment center for a television. You need to know the width, height, and diagonal of the television. The width of the television is 36 inches. The length of the diagonal of the television is 45 inches. Determine the height of the television.

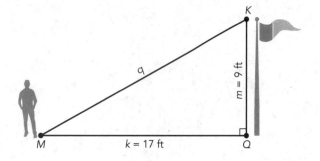

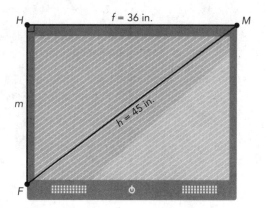

Name _____   Date _____

7. Clayton is responsible for changing the broken light bulb in a streetlamp. The streetlamp is 12 feet high. Clayton places the base of his ladder 4 feet from the base of the streetlamp. Clayton can extend his ladder from 10 feet to 14 feet. How long must his ladder be to reach the top of the streetlamp? Round your answer to the nearest hundredth of a foot.

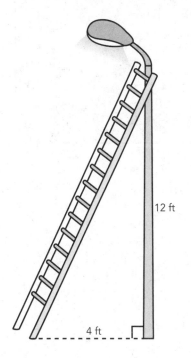

8. Jada is helping to build a swing set at the community park. The swing bar at the top of the set should be 8 feet from the ground. The base of the support beam extends 3 feet from the plane of the swing bar. How long should each support beam be? Round your answer to the nearest tenth of foot.

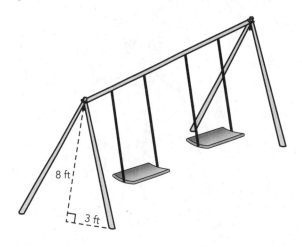

9. Perry wants to replace the net on his basketball hoop. The hoop is 10 feet high. Perry places his ladder 4 feet from the base of the hoop. How long must his ladder be to reach the hoop? Round your answer to the nearest hundredth of a foot.

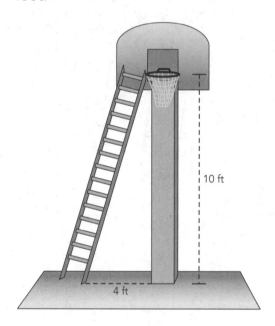

10. Ling wants to create a diagonal path through her flower garden using stepping stones. She would like to place one stone every 2 feet. How many stepping stones does she need?

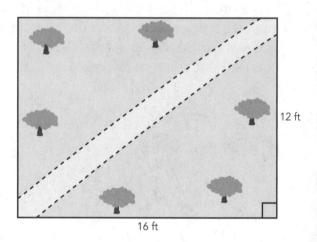

Name _____   Date _____

11. Firefighters need to cross from the roof of a 25-foot-tall building to the roof of a 35-foot-tall building by using a ladder. The buildings are 20 feet apart. To the nearest whole foot, what minimum length does the ladder need to be in order to span the two buildings?

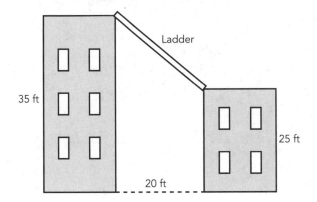

12. Chen is building a ramp for his remote control car. He wants the end of the ramp to extend 4 feet from the base of the ramp. The base of the ramp is 18 inches high. How long should the piece of wood for the ramp be? Round your answer to the nearest tenth of an inch.

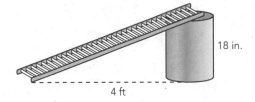

III. Calculating Distances on the Coordinate Plane

A. Calculate the distance from *A* to *B* in each diagram. Write your answer as a radical if necessary.

1.

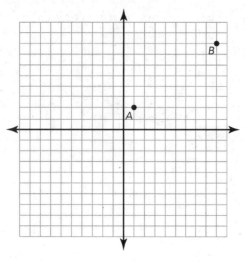

2.

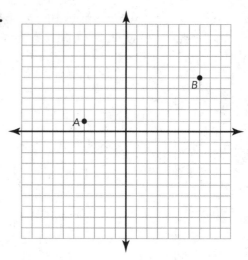

3.

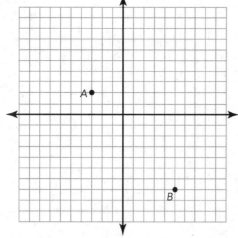

4.

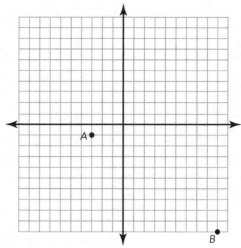

Name _____   Date _____

5.

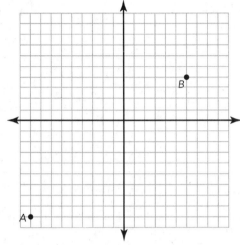

6.

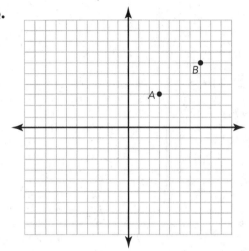

7.

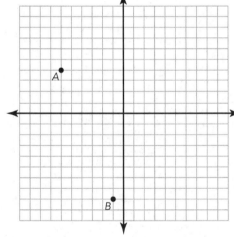

8.

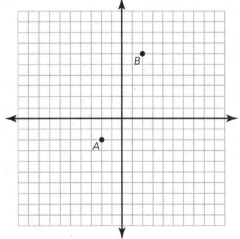

9.

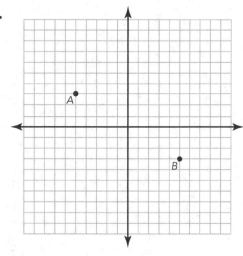

10.

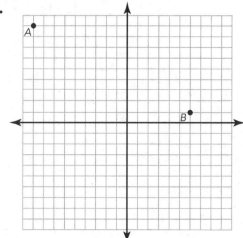

11.

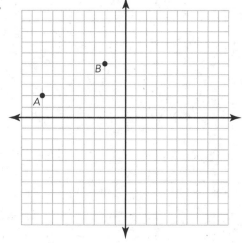

12.

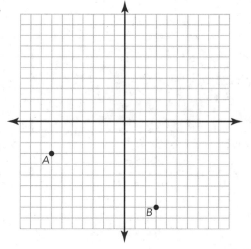

Topic 1
Exponents and Scientific Notation

Name _____ Date _____

I. Using the Product Rule and the Quotient Rule
A. Simplify each expression completely.

1. $2n^4m^3 \cdot 19n^2m^9$

2. $\dfrac{17k^5x^3}{19k^9x}$

3. $3n^5z^9(-5)n^3z^6$

4. $\dfrac{15wa^5}{-6w^5a^8}$

5. $\dfrac{-5m^9d^4}{-11m^3d}$

6. $(-3b^5k)(9b^5k^3)$

7. $-\dfrac{8c^8k^5}{2c^9k^2}$

8. $(-3k^5w^3)(-13)k^7w^9$

9. $\dfrac{9z^5a^6}{16z^6a^7}$

10. $(-5n^7j^6)(16n^7j^6)$

11. $\dfrac{12n^5m^3}{-12n^9m^5}$

12. $\dfrac{8w^9m^5}{20wm^9}$

13. $(-8w^5d^6)(11w^4d^3)$

14. $-\dfrac{3bx^6}{12b^4x^8}$

15. $3k^4m^6 \cdot 18k^9m^4$

16. $-y^2x^6 \cdot 8y^8x^6$

17. $\dfrac{-20c^7b^3}{-10c^2b^4}$

18. $(-7a^9z^8)(7a^4z^7)$

II. Using the Power to a Power Rule
A. Simplify each expression completely.

1. $(m^6)^4$

2. $(n^8)^2$

3. $(d^5)^5$

4. $(m^3)^6$

5. $(z^5)^2$

6. $(x^2)^9$

7. $(y^4)^4$

8. $(a^2)^3$

9. $(b^3)^5$

10. $(c^5)^4$

11. $(f^3)^7$

12. $(w^2)^6$

13. $(k^3)^4$

14. $(g^6)^6$

15. $(s^8)^5$

16. $(h^9)^3$

17. $(u^2)^7$

18. $(j^8)^3$

III. Using the Product to a Power Rule and the Quotient to a Power Rule

A. Simplify each expression completely. Assume that variables are not zero.

1. $(3d^7x^3)^3$

2. $\left(\dfrac{x^3}{a^5}\right)^4$

3. $(-k^4w^9x)^2$

4. $-(-4c^6d^7a^4)^3$

5. $\left(\dfrac{x^3}{c^3}\right)^7$

6. $\left(\dfrac{c}{b}\right)^5$

7. $(-4a^5y^2k^5)^3$

8. $\left(\dfrac{n^9}{m^3}\right)^2$

9. $(6y^2z^9)^2$

10. $-(5ac^2)^2$

11. $\left(\dfrac{a}{d^2}\right)^9$

12. $-(-2w^2k^3x^4)^3$

13. $(a^8x^7b^3)^2$

14. $\left(\dfrac{b^2}{j^3}\right)^4$

15. $\left(\dfrac{k^5}{c}\right)^3$

16. $-(-cb^7)^3$

17. $\left(\dfrac{n^6}{b^7}\right)^2$

18. $(-6n^9yj)^2$

IV. Simplifying Expressions with Negative and Zero Exponents

A. Simplify each expression completely.

1. $-11n^{-4}$

2. $\dfrac{11}{17n^{-4}}$

3. $\dfrac{-10}{-2y^{-4}}$

4. $14c^0$

5. $17z^{-7}$

6. $\dfrac{7}{-18y^{-8}}$

7. $\dfrac{16}{19t^0}$

8. $6n^{-9}$

9. $3x^{-4}$

10. $-\dfrac{5}{(a^{-9})}$

11. $-\dfrac{6}{5d^{-2}}$

12. $-\dfrac{3}{16s^0}$

13. $-20x^0$

14. $-5z^{-3}$

15. $\dfrac{15}{-10n^0}$

16. $-11w^{-6}$

17. $\dfrac{14}{-7b^{-1}}$

18. $5a^0$

Name _____   Date _____

V. Using Scientific Notation

A. Write each number in scientific notation.

1. 852,000   **2.** 90,000,000   **3.** 30,000

4. 7,710,000   **5.** 73,500,000   **6.** 7,000,000,000

7. 884,000,000   **8.** 498,000   **9.** 9,540,000

10. 0.03   **11.** 0.964   **12.** 0.056

13. 0.008   **14.** 0.000095   **15.** 0.306

16. 0.000000772   **17.** 0.000004   **18.** 0.0001977

B. Write each number in standard form.

1. $3 \cdot 10^4$ **2.** $4.14 \cdot 10$ **3.** $2 \cdot 10^{-4}$

4. $8.38 \cdot 10^{-3}$ **5.** $1.33 \cdot 10^5$ **6.** $2.56 \cdot 10^{10}$

7. $6 \cdot 10^9$ **8.** $6.48 \cdot 10^{-5}$ **9.** $5 \cdot 10^{-3}$

10. $1.2 \cdot 10^{-6}$ **11.** $9.56 \cdot 10^{-4}$ **12.** $8.81 \cdot 10^6$

13. $9 \cdot 10^7$ **14.** $3.8 \cdot 10^{-8}$ **15.** $1 \cdot 10^{-7}$

16. $4 \cdot 10^8$ **17.** $5.09 \cdot 10^5$ **18.** $2.11 \cdot 10^{-1}$

VI. Comparing Numbers Using Scientific Notation

A. Write > or < to compare each pair of numbers.

1. 4.5×10^7 ___ 4.5×10^6 **2.** 1.4×10^{-8} ___ 8.6×10^{-4} **3.** 7.3×10^{-6} ___ 1.5×10^{-6}

4. 2.2×10^{12} ___ 9.5×10^4 **5.** 1.9×10^{-5} ___ 6.5×10^{-5} **6.** 3.7×10^{-2} ___ 9.9×10^{-9}

7. 9.1×10^5 ___ 3.5×10^3 **8.** 8.4×10^{-2} ___ 8.04×10^{-2} **9.** 1.1×10^{-9} ___ 9.9×10^1

10. 1.1×10^{-9} ___ 9.9×10^{-1} **11.** 6.4×10^4 ___ 6.09×10^4 **12.** 1.3×10^{-7} ___ 9.1×10^{-7}

B. Complete each sentence.

1. 5.61×10^9 is about _____ times the value of 8.38×10^8

2. 7.5946×10^{-2} is about _____ times the value of 1.8×10^{-3}

3. 1.0×10^{-5} is about _____ times the value of 9.6×10^{-11}

4. 9.3×10^7 is about _____ times the value of 2.39×10^5

5. 2.5×10^{-2} is about _____ times the value of 5.85×10^{-5}

6. 3.45×10^{12} is about _____ times the value of 1.5×10^8

7. 4.5703×10^{-3} is about _____ times the value of 2.02×10^{-5}

8. 5.9×10^{-7} is about _____ times the value of 7.4×10^{-8}

9. 6.0×10^5 is about _____ times the value of 1.2×10^{-3}

10. 8.59×10^{20} is about _____ times the value of 9.04×10^{17}

11. 7.6×10^{-13} is about _____ times the value of 9.265×10^{-14}

12. 3.12×10^2 is about _____ times the value of 1.29×10^{-7}

Topic 2
Volume of Curved Figures

Name _____ Date _____

I. Volume of Cylinders

A. Solve each problem.

1. The local deli sells sandwich pepperoni. The pepperoni comes in the form of a cylinder. The radius of the pepperoni is 22 millimeters and the height of the pepperoni is 110 millimeters. What is the volume of the pepperoni?

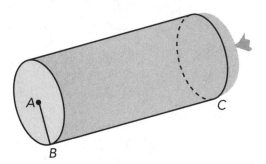

2. You like to eat oatmeal for breakfast. The oatmeal container is a cylinder. The radius of the container is 5.1 centimeters and the height of the container is 22.3 centimeters. What is the volume of the container?

3. The local deli sells cheese wheels. Each cheese wheel is a cylinder. The height of the cheese wheel is 2.8 inches and the volume of the cheese wheel is 155.09088 cubic inches. What is the radius of the cheese wheel?

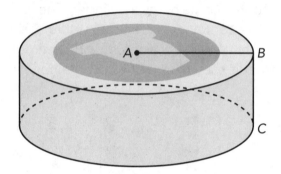

4. Your uncle has a sculpture displayed on a display stand. The display stand is a cylinder. The radius of the display stand is 8.7 centimeters and the height of the display stand is 27.8 centimeters. What is the volume of the display stand?

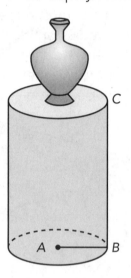

5. The given figure is a cylinder. The radius of the cylinder is 6 inches and the height of the cylinder is 24 inches. What is the volume of the cylinder?

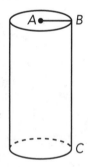

6. Your aunt keeps a candle on her nightstand. The candle is a cylinder. The radius of the candle is 3.2 centimeters and the volume of the candle is 302.24384 cubic centimeters. What is the height of the candle?

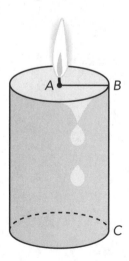

Name _____ Date _____

7. The given figure is a cylinder. The radius of the cylinder is 4.8 inches and the height of the cylinder is 15.8 inches. What is the volume of the cylinder?

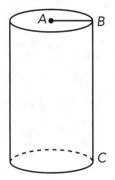

8. The given figure is a cylinder. The radius of the cylinder is 8 feet and the height of the cylinder is 24 feet. What is the volume of the cylinder?

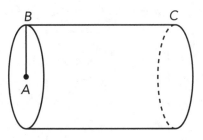

9. The local library has a number of pillars at the front entrance. Each pillar is a cylinder. The radius of each pillar is 17 inches and the volume of each pillar is 231,402.3 cubic inches. What is the height of each pillar?

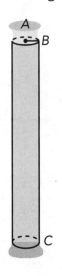

10. The given figure is a cylinder. The radius of the cylinder is 2 millimeters and the height of the cylinder is 4 millimeters. What is the volume of the cylinder?

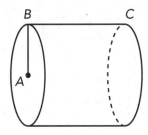

11. The given figure is a cylinder. The radius of the cylinder is 6.1 feet and the height of the cylinder is 16.9 feet. What is the volume of the cylinder?

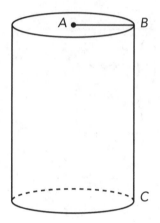

12. You are helping your uncle chop firewood into logs. Each log is a cylinder. The height of each log is 16.5 inches and the volume of each log is 1803.5061 cubic inches. What is the radius of each log?

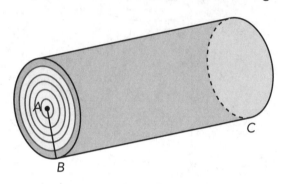

13. The given figure is a cylinder. The radius of the cylinder is 6.4 feet and the height of the cylinder is 7.3 feet. What is the volume of the cylinder?

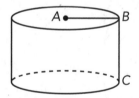

14. The given figure is a cylinder. The radius of the cylinder is 5.4 inches and the height of the cylinder is 25.6 inches. What is the volume of the cylinder?

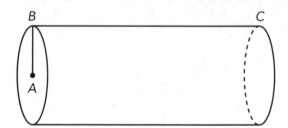

Name _____   Date _____

15. You buy a can of soup at the supermarket. The soup can is a cylinder. The height of the can is 15.7 centimeters and the volume of the can is 749.82258 cubic centimeters. What is the radius of the can?

16. The given figure is a cylinder. The radius of the cylinder is 2.3 millimeters and the height of the cylinder is 15.6 millimeters. What is the volume of the cylinder?

II. Volume of Cones

A. Solve each problem.

1. You buy your aunt a new drill bit set. Each drill bit is a cone. The radius of the drill bit is 3.9 millimeters and the height of the drill bit is 7.7 millimeters. What is the volume of the drill bit?

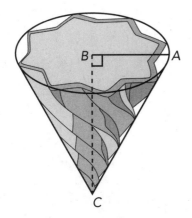

2. The local museum has a teepee on display. The teepee is a cone. The radius of the teepee is 4.7 feet and the height of the teepee is 17.8 feet. What is the volume of the teepee?

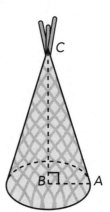

3. A silo is used to store harvested crops such as corn. The silo roof is a cone. The radius of the silo roof is 5.9 feet and the height of the silo roof is 11.8 feet. What is the volume of the silo roof?

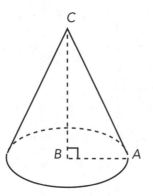

4. Your aunt bought a new umbrella. The umbrella is a cone. The height of the umbrella is 8 inches and volume of the umbrella is 4429.4933 cubic inches. What is the radius of the umbrella?

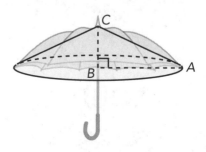

5. The given figure is a cone. The radius of the cone is 9 inches and the height of the cone is 36 inches. What is the volume of the cone?

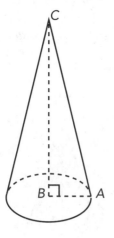

6. The given figure is a cone. The radius of the cone is 7.8 inches and the height of the cone is 25.2 inches. What is the volume of the cone?

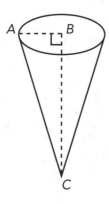

Name _____   Date _____

7. The given figure is a cone. The radius of the cone is 13 feet and the height of the cone is 39 feet. What is the volume of the cone?

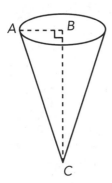

8. Your gym teacher uses traffic cones to create part of an obstacle course. The radius of the traffic cone is 6.4 inches and the volume of the traffic cone is 1045.5335 cubic inches. What is the height of the traffic cone?

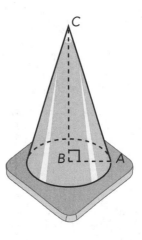

9. The given figure is a cone. The radius of the cone is 3 millimeters and the height of the cone is 6 millimeters. What is the volume of the cone?

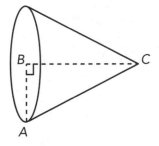

10. The given figure is a cone. The radius of the cone is 10.2 feet and the height of the cone is 28.1 feet. What is the volume of the cone?

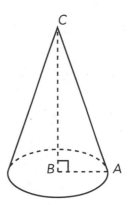

11. The given figure is a cone. The radius of the cone is 11 feet and the height of the cone is 12.5 feet. What is the volume of the cone?

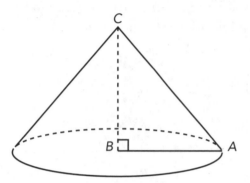

12. You and your friends buy ice cream cones at the local ice cream shop. The radius of the ice cream cone is 44 millimeters and volume of the ice cream cone is 356,456.2136 cubic millimeters. What is the height of the ice cream cone?

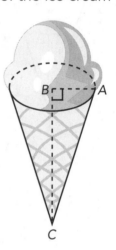

13. The given figure is a cone. The radius of the cone is 10.7 millimeters and the height of the cone is 52.8 millimeters. What is the volume of the cone?

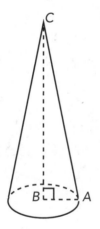

14. The given figure is a cone. The radius of the cone is 2.1 feet and the height of the cone is 7.5 feet. What is the volume of the cone?

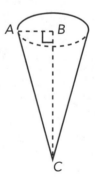

Name _____   Date _____

15. The school cheerleading team uses megaphones in their routines. Each megaphone is a cone. The radius of the megaphone is 5.1 inches and the height of the megaphone is 19.3 inches. What is the volume of the megaphone?

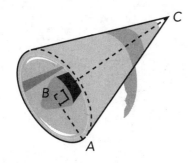

16. Your uncle uses a funnel to change the oil in his car. The funnel is a cone. The height of the funnel is 10.6 centimeters and the volume of the funnel is 335.6137 cubic centimeters. What is the radius of the funnel?

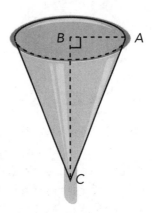

III. Volume of Spheres

A. Solve each problem.

1. Kickball is a popular playground sport among younger children. A kickball is a sphere. The volume of the kickball is 1203.6499 cubic inches. What is the radius of the kickball?

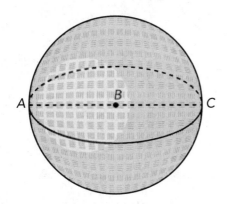

2. You play volleyball in gym class. The volleyball is a sphere. The radius of the volleyball is 10.7 centimeters. What is the volume of the volleyball?

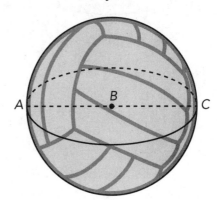

3. Your family decides to attend a baseball game. During the fifth inning, you catch a foul ball. The baseball is a sphere. The radius of the baseball is 36.6 millimeters. What is the volume of the baseball?

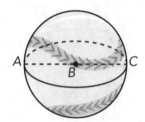

4. The given figure is a sphere. The radius of the sphere is 24 centimeters. What is the volume of the sphere?

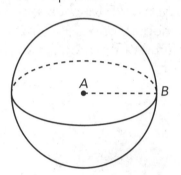

5. Your history teacher has a globe of Earth in the classroom. The globe is a sphere. The volume of the globe is 33,493.3333 cubic centimeters. What is the radius of the globe?

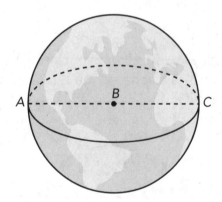

6. Your aunt buys a new pool table. Each billiards ball is a sphere. The radius of each billiards ball is 28 millimeters. What is the volume of each billiards ball?

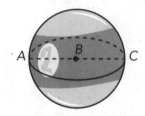

Name _____   Date _____

7. The given figure is a sphere. The radius
of the sphere is 22 meters. What is the
volume of the sphere?

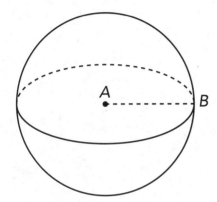

8. The given figure is a sphere. The radius
of the sphere is 20 millimeters. What is
the volume of the sphere?

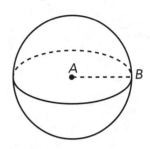

9. You decided to try out for the school
basketball team. A basketball is a sphere.
The volume of the basketball is 4846.59
cubic centimeters. What is the radius of
the basketball?

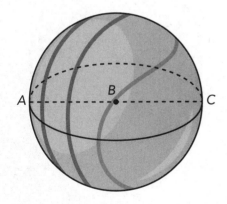

10. The given figure is a sphere. The radius
of the sphere is 23 meters. What is the
volume of the sphere?

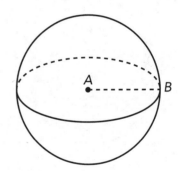

11. The given figure is a sphere. The radius of the sphere is 21 centimeters. What is the volume of the sphere?

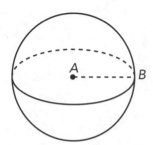

12. The given figure is a sphere. The radius of the sphere is 7 feet. What is the volume of the sphere?

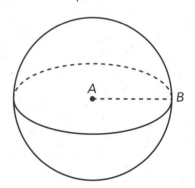

13. You and a friend go miniature golfing. A golf ball is a sphere. The volume of the golf ball is 42,191.9539 cubic millimeters. What is the radius of the golf ball?

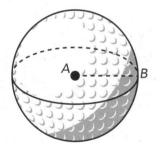

14. You enjoy playing soccer with your friends. A soccer ball is a sphere. The radius of the soccer ball is 5.2 inches. What is the volume of the soccer ball?

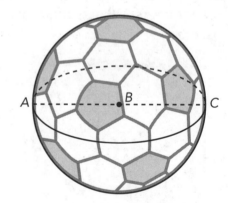

Name _____ Date _____

15. The given figure is a sphere. The radius of the sphere is 8 inches. What is the volume of the sphere?

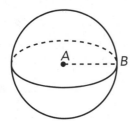

16. The given figure is a sphere. The radius of the sphere is 18 meters. What is the volume of the sphere?

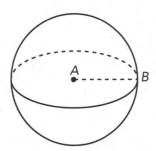

MODULE 1

Topic 1

Rigid Motion Transformations

I. A.

1. horizontal translation of −2 units

3. vertical translation of 7 units

5. vertical translation of 5 units

II. A.

1. reflection across the y-axis

3. reflection across the x-axis

5. reflection across the x-axis

III. A.

1. rotation counterclockwise 90°

3. rotation 180°

5. rotation counterclockwise 90°

Topic 2

Similarity

I. A.

1.

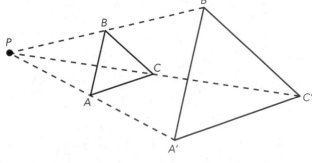

3.

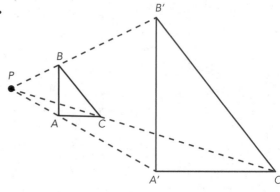

5.

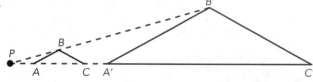

II. A.

1. dilation of $\frac{1}{3}$

3. dilation of $\frac{1}{2}$

5. dilation of 3

III. A.

1. center of dilation: X; dilation of 2; reflection about the line $y = 2$

3. center of dilation: A; dilation of $\frac{1}{2}$; rotation 180°

5. center of dilation: Q; dilation of 3; horizontal translation of −30 units

7. center of dilation: Q; dilation of 3; vertical translation of −8 units

9. center of dilation: X; dilation of 3; rotation 180°

11. reflection about the line $y = -5$; rotation counterclockwise 90°; center of dilation: A; dilation of 2

Topic 3

Line and Angle Relationships

I. A.

Answers will vary.

1. $\angle 3$ and $\angle 4$

3. $\angle 9$ and $\angle 10$

5. $\angle 17$ and $\angle 18$

I. B.

1. Monroe Dr., Roosevelt Ave., Polk Way

3. Wilson Ave., Hoover Ave., Roosevelt Ave.

5. $\angle 16$ and $\angle 25$

7. $\angle 7$, $\angle 15$, $\angle 21$, and $\angle 23$

I. C.

1. linear

3. same-side exterior

5. alternate interior

7. same-side exterior

9. linear

11. same-side interior

I. D.

1. $\angle 2$, $\angle 4$, and $\angle 8$
5. $\angle 2$, $\angle 4$, $\angle 6$, and $\angle 8$

3. There are no angles that are neither congruent nor supplementary to $\angle 6$.

II. A.

1. linear; 74°

3. linear; 74°

5. same-side interior; 74°

III. A.

Answers will vary.

1.

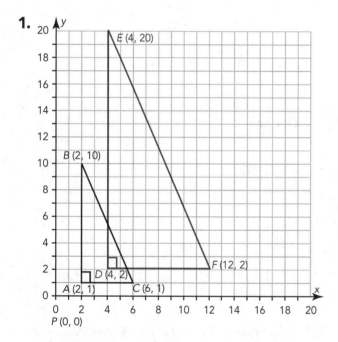

$\angle A$ and $\angle D$ are both right angles so they are corresponding angles. The measures of $\angle B$ and $\angle E$ are equal. The two triangles are similar.

3.

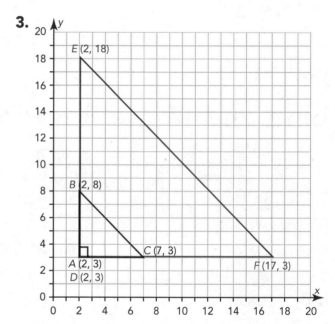

$\angle A$ and $\angle D$ are the same angle and have the same measure. The measures of $\angle B$ and $\angle E$ are equal. The two triangles are similar.

5.

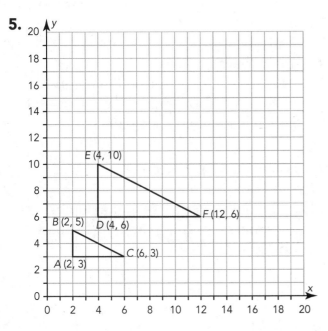

∠A and ∠D are both right angles and have the same measure. The measures of ∠B and ∠E are equal. The two triangles are similar.

MODULE 2

Topic 1

From Proportions to Linear Relationships

I. A.

1a. $y = 25x$

1b. 175 signatures

1c. 9 sheets

1d. 25; For each increase in the number of sheets filled, the number of signatures increases by 25.

3a. $y = 110x$

3b. 550 calories

3c. 3.5 hours

3d. 110; For each increase in the number of miles run, the number of calories burned increases by 110.

5a. $y = 4x$

5b. 100 units

5c. 33 kumquat trees

5d. 4; For each increase in the number of kumquat trees planted, the number of units of land used increases by 4.

9a. $y = 8x$

9b. $200

9c. 37.5 hours

9d. 8; For each increase in the number of hours worked, the amount of money earned increases by $8.

7a. $y = 350x$

7b. 3150 pages

7c. 16 "perfect books"

7d. 350; For each increase in the number of "perfect books" read, the number of pages read increases by 350.

11a. $y = 10x$

11b. 5 minutes (300 seconds)

11c. 33 combinations

11d. 10; For each increase in the number of combinations tried, the time increases by 10 seconds.

II. A.

1a. $y = 8.5x$

1b. 76.5 yards

1c. 19 windows

1d. 8.5; For each increase in the number of windows, the number of yards of fabric increases by 8.5.

5a. $y = \frac{1}{2}x$

5b. 7 hours

5c. 38 documents

5d. $\frac{1}{2}$; For each increase in the number of documents translated, the time increases by $\frac{1}{2}$ hour.

9a. $y = \frac{2}{3}x$

9b. 54 players

9c. 36 players

9d. $\frac{2}{3}$; For every three players who try out, the number of players who make the team increases by 2.

3a. $y = 0.15x$

3b. $9

3c. 235 signatures

3d. 0.15; For each increase in the number of signatures, the amount of money made increases by $0.15.

7a. $y = \frac{1}{3}x$

7b. 3 gallons

7c. 16 days

7d. $\frac{1}{3}$; For each increase in the number of days since being planted, the number of gallons of water provided increases by $\frac{1}{3}$.

11a. $y = 0.1x$

11b. $18

11c. 65 miles

11d. 0.1; For each increase in the number of miles driven, the amount of the toll bill increases by $0.10.

III. A.

1a. $y = \dfrac{550 + x}{4}$

1b. $180

1c. $90

1d. $\dfrac{1}{4}$; For every $4 the price of the printer increases, the amount owed each month increases by $1.

3a. $y = \dfrac{300 - x}{5}$

3b. $50

3c. $90

3d. $-\dfrac{1}{5}$; For every $5 he gives his brother, Santo saves $1 fewer each week.

5a. $y = \dfrac{25 + x}{5}$

5b. 17 balances

5c. 70 balances

5d. $\dfrac{1}{5}$; For every 5 balances the school receives, the number of balances in each lab increases by 1.

7a. $y = \dfrac{100 + x}{2}$

7b. 78 passengers

7c. 76 tickets

7d. $\dfrac{1}{2}$; For every two tickets sold, the number of passengers in each bus increases by 1.

9a. $y = \dfrac{12 + x}{8}$

9b. 7 slices

9c. 36 slices

9d. $\dfrac{1}{8}$; For every 8 orange slices brought by the parents, the number of slices each player receives increases by 1.

11a. $y = \dfrac{x + 1260}{3}$

11b. $1030

11c. $3030

11d. $\dfrac{1}{3}$; For every $3 received after the first week, the amount of money placed in each account increases by $1.

Topic 2

Linear Relationships

I. A.

1. 0

7. -1

3. $-\dfrac{5}{12}$

9. $-\dfrac{4}{9}$

5. $\dfrac{5}{9}$

11. $\dfrac{1}{3}$

II. A.

1a. $y = 84 - 2x$

1b.

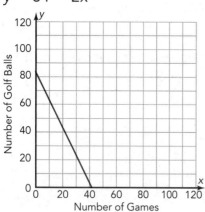

1c. The slope is −2 and the y-intercept is 84. The y-intercept means that Karl begins with 84 golf balls. The slope means that he loses 2 golf balls per game played.

3a. $y = 24.75 + 0.2x$

3b.

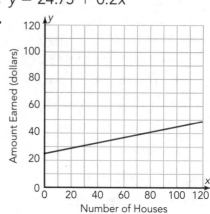

3c. The slope is 0.2 and the y-intercept is 24.75. The y-intercept means that Jordan begins by making $24.75 before delivering to any houses. The slope means that her pay increases by $0.20 for every house she delivers to.

5a. $y = 48 + 24x$

5b.

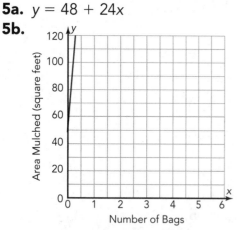

5c. The slope is 24 and the y-intercept is 48. The y-intercept means that 48 square feet of garden have already been covered in mulch. The slope means that there are 24 more square feet of garden covered by each additional bag of mulch.

7a. $y = 5 + 3.9x$

7b.

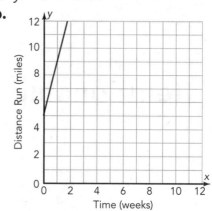

7c. The slope is 3.9 and the y-intercept is 5. The y-intercept means that in week 0 you only run 5 miles. The slope means that for each additional week you run, the distance you run increases by 3.9 miles.

9a. $y = 75 - 3x$

9b.

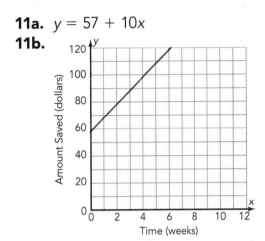

Number of Games Remaining (y-axis, values 0 to 120)
Time (weeks) (x-axis, values 0 to 30)

9c. The slope is −3 and the y-intercept is 75. The y-intercept means that Shona expects the bat to last for 75 games. The slope means that for each week that passes, there are 3 fewer games left for her to use the bat.

11a. $y = 57 + 10x$

11b.

Amount Saved (dollars) (y-axis, values 0 to 120)
Time (weeks) (x-axis, values 0 to 12)

11c. The slope is 10 and the y-intercept is 57. The y-intercept means that Marcos has already save $57. The slope means that for each week that passes, Marcos saves an additional $10.

13a. $y = 13x + 9.95$

13b.

Total Cost (dollars) (y-axis, values 0 to 120)
Number of Students (x-axis, values 0 to 12)

13c. The slope is 13 and the y-intercept is 9.95. The y-intercept means there will be a cost of $9.95 before tickets are purchased. The slope means that the total cost will increase by $13 for each student that buys a ticket.

15a. $y = 34 + 5x$

15b.

Number of Nature Photos (y-axis, values 0 to 120)
Time (days) (x-axis, values 0 to 12)

15c. The slope is 5 and the y-intercept is 34. The y-intercept means that Lamar has already taken 34 photos. The slope means that for each day he takes photos, his number of nature photos increases by 5.

17a. $y = 0.5 + 0.4x$

17b.

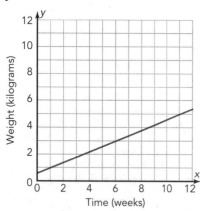

17c. The slope is 0.4 and the y-intercept is 0.5. The y-intercept means that the polar bear starts with a weight of 0.5 kg. The slope means that for each additional week, the weight of the polar bear increases by 0.4 kg.

19a. $y = 140 - 9x$

19b.

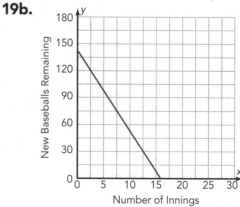

19c. The slope is -9 and the y-intercept is 140. The y-intercept means that the game begins with 140 new baseballs. The slope means the for every inning played, there are 9 fewer new baseballs.

III. A.

1a. $(0, -6)$

1b. Sample answer: $(1, -9)$

1c.

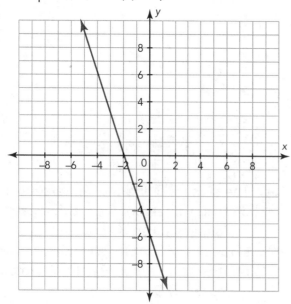

3a. $(0, 4)$

3b. Sample answer: $(2, 6)$

3c.

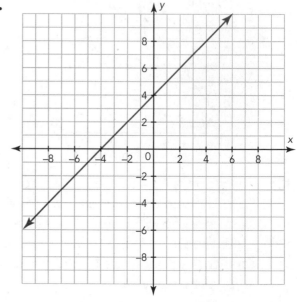

5a. (0, 5)
5b. Sample answer: (1, 7)
5c.

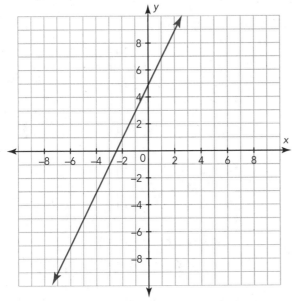

7a. (0, −1)
7b. Sample answer: (1, 3)
7c.

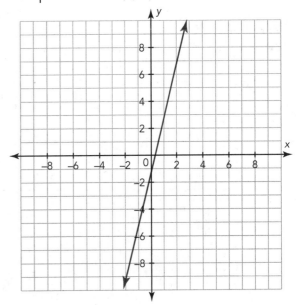

9a. (0, −2)
9b. Sample answer: (1, −3)
9c.

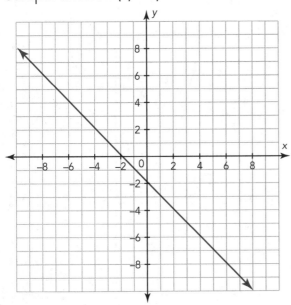

11a. (0, 4)
11b. Sample answer: (1, −1)
11c.

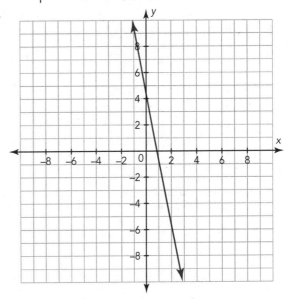

III. B.

1a. (1, 2)
1b. Sample answer: (2, 4)
1c.

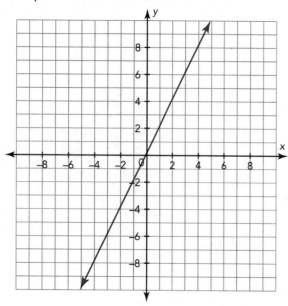

3a. (−1, 5)
3b. Sample answer: (0, 8)
3c.

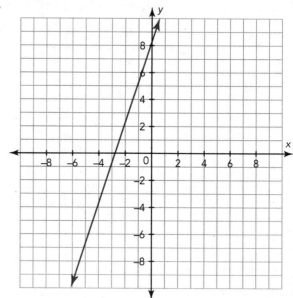

5a. (1, 4)
5b. Sample answer: (2, 1)
5c.

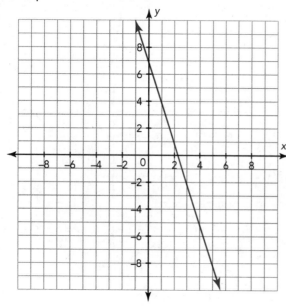

7a. (−4, 2)
7b. Sample answer: (−3, −2)
7c.

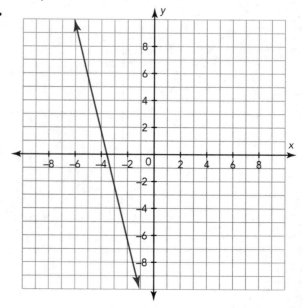

9a. (4, 3)
9b. Sample answer:
9c.

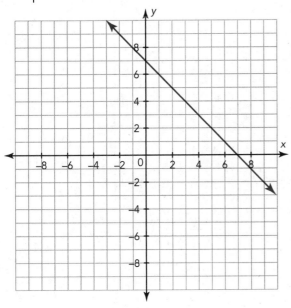

11a. (−3, 6)
11b. Sample answer: (−2, 8)
11c.

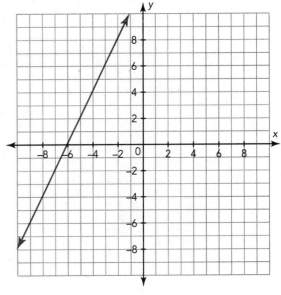

III. C.

1a. (6, 0)
1b. (0, 5)
1c.

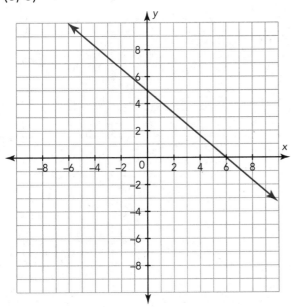

3a. (10, 0)
3b. (0, 6)
3c.

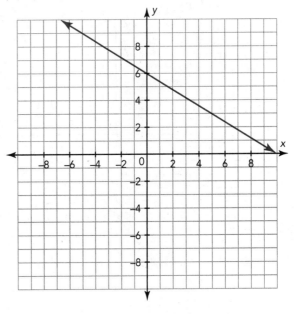

5a. (−4, 0)
5b. (0, 7)
5c.

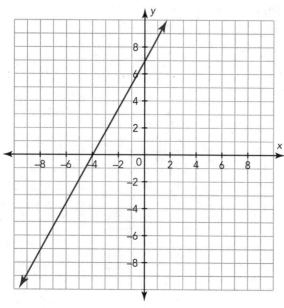

7a. (−8, 0)
7b. (0, −4)
7c.

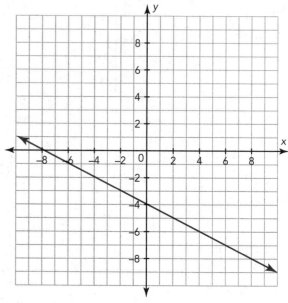

9a. (5, 0)
9b. (0, −6)
9c.

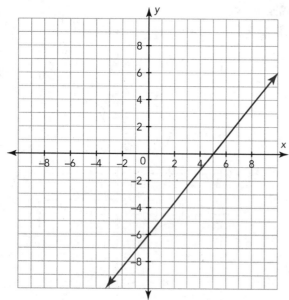

11a. (−7, 0)
11b. (0, −2)
11c.

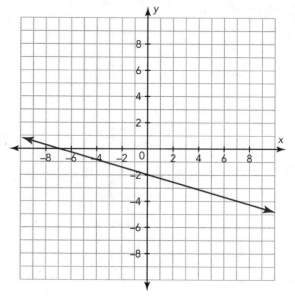

IV. A.

1. $y = x + 12$

3. $y = \frac{6}{5}x - \frac{2}{5}$

5. $y = -\frac{5}{4}x - \frac{9}{2}$

7. $y = -\frac{7}{6}x + \frac{8}{3}$

9. $y = \frac{7}{6}x + \frac{13}{6}$

11. $y = \frac{11}{8}x - \frac{47}{8}$

V. A.

1a. Let x represent the time in hours spent pulling up flooring and y represent the time worked each day in hours. The equation is $y = \frac{12 + x}{10}$.

1b.

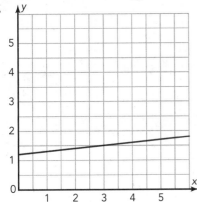

1c. 1.6 hours

3a. Let x represent the time in weeks and y represent the number of rabbits. The equation is $y = 11 + x$.

3b.

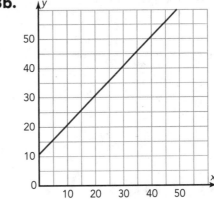

3c. 4 weeks

5a. Let x represent the time in weeks and y represent the number of LED bulbs. The equation is $y = 7 + x$.

5b.

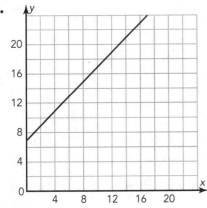

5c. 37 LED bulbs

7a. Let x represent the price in dollars per pound and y represent the amount spent. The equation is $y = 6x$.

7b.

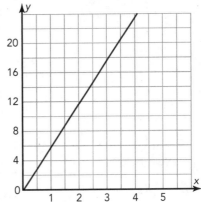

7c. $1.40 per pound

9a. Let x represent the amount in inches of blue ribbon and y represent the total amount in inches of ribbon. The equation is $y = x + 11.2$.

9b.

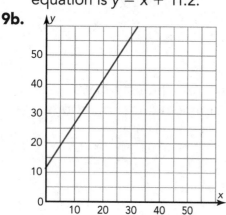

9c. 8.3 inches

11a. Let x represent the time in years since the company began and y represent the financial status of the company in millions of dollars. The equation is $y = -1.2 + 0.6x$.

11b.

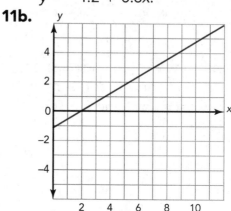

11c. 2 years

Topic 3

Introduction to Functions

I. A.

1. $f(x) = 2x + 30$

5. $f(x) = 2x - 100$

9. $f(x) = 2x + 100$

13. $f(x) = -\frac{3}{4}x - 75$

3. $f(x) = -x - 50$

7. $f(x) = -\frac{1}{2}x + 3$

11. $f(x) = -2x + 9$

15. $f(x) = 4x + 25$

II. A.

1. (1, 4), (2, 6), (3, 8), (4, 10)
The relation is a function.

5. (0, 4), (1, 4), (2, 4), (3, 4)
The relation is a function.

9. (5, 0), (5, 1), (5, 2), (5, 3), (5, 4)
The relation is not a function.

3. (5, 20), (6, 10), (7, 10), (8, 30), (10, 30)
The relation is a function.

7. (15, 0), (10, 5), (5, 10), (10, 15), (15, 20)
The relation is not a function.

II. B.

1. Yes. Each friend receives just 1 valentine from Lila.

5. No. Each showing is mapped to over 200 people.

9. No. One flight is mapped to 350 people.

3. No. One memo is mapped to 28 teachers.

7. No. The new issue is mailed to millions of readers.

II. C.

1. The scatter plot is not a function. A vertical line can be drawn through (4, 1) and (4, 5).

3. The scatter plot is not a function. A vertical line can be drawn through (3, 2), and (3, 6).

5. The scatter plot is a function. No vertical lines cross more than one point.

7. The graph is a function. No vertical line will cross two y-values for any x-value.

9. The graph is not a function. A vertical line will cross all y-values for x-values of 8.

II. D.

1. The equation is a function.

3. The equation is not a function. Each x-value except 0 can be mapped to two y-values.

5. The equation is a function.

7. The equation is a function.

9. The equation is a function.

III. A.

1a. (4, 0)
1b. (0, 6)
1c. all real numbers
1d. all real numbers
1e. negative

3a. There is no x-intercept.
3b. (0, 7)
3c. all real numbers
3d. $y = 7$
3e. 0

5a. (5, 0)
5b. (0, 5)
5c. all real numbers
5d. all real numbers
5e. negative

7a. (5, 0)
7b. (0, −9)
7c. all real numbers
7d. all real numbers
7e. positive

9a. (−5, 0)
9b. (0, −6)
9c. all real numbers
9d. all real numbers
9e. negative

11a. (−6, 0)
11b. (0, −4)
11c. all real numbers
11d. all real numbers
11e. negative

Topic 4

Patterns in Bivariate Data

I. A.

1. negative linear association

3. positive linear association

5. non-linear linear association

7. no association

9. negative linear association

11. no association

II. A.

1. Answers will vary but should be close to the following.

Slope: 2

y-intercept: −7

Line of best fit equation: $y = 2x - 7$

3. Answers will vary but should be close to the following.

Slope: 7

y-intercept: −12

Line of best fit equation: $y = 7x - 12$

5. Answers will vary but should be close to the following.

Slope: 1

y-intercept: 1

Line of best fit equation: $y = x + 1$

7. Answers will vary but should be close to the following.

Slope: $-\frac{1}{2}$

y-intercept: 10

Line of best fit equation: $y = -\frac{1}{2}x + 10$

9. Answers will vary but should be close to the following.

Slope: 1

y-intercept: -5

Line of best fit equation: $y = x - 5$

11. Answers will vary but should be close to the following.

Slope: $\frac{1}{2}$

y-intercept: 0

Line of best fit equation: $y = \frac{1}{2}x$

II. B.

1. The grocery store earns $120 if they sell 200 tomatoes.

5. There will be 2000 gallons of water in the pool after 200 minutes.

3. The car used 4 gallons of gas.

MODULE 3

Topic 1

Solving Linear Equations

I. A.

1. $q = 1$

3. $a = 3$

5. $b = 2$

I. B.

1. $x = 12$

3. $t = 45$

5. $n = -150$

I. C.

1. c

3. f

5. g

7. a

II. A.

1. $x = 4$

3. $x = -1$

5. $x = 3$

7. $x = 2$

9. $x = \frac{5}{18}$

11. $x = \frac{4}{5}$

III. A.

1. no solutions   **3.** infinite solutions   **5.** no solutions
7. one solution   **9.** one solution   **11.** one solution
13. one solution   **15.** no solutions   **17.** no solutions
19. infinite solutions   **21.** one solution   **23.** infinite solutions

III. B.

1. $x = 2$; one solution

5. $x = 3$; one solution

9. $4x + 3 = 4x + 3$ or $0 = 0$; infinite solutions

3. $7 = 20$; no solutions

7. $10x + 10 = 10x + 10$ or $0 = 0$; infinite solutions

11. $x = \frac{1}{2}$; one solution

Topic 2

Systems of Linear Equations

I. A.

1.

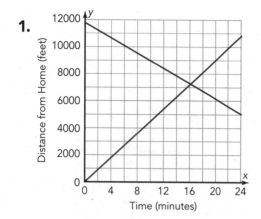

a. Shawn was 2700 feet from home and Dante was 10,000 feet from home.
b. Dante was 8320 feet from home after walking for 12 minutes.
c. The boys met after walking for 16 minutes.

3.

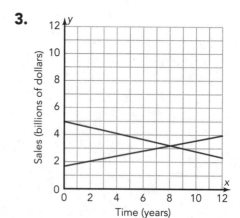

a. Computer Company A's predicted total sales are $2.94 billion and Computer Company B's predicted total sales are $3.35 billion.
b. 3 years
c. 8 years

5.

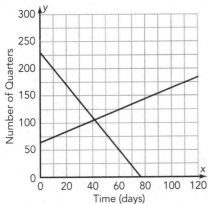

a. Jean will have 74 quarters and Brian will have 198 quarters
b. 76 days
c. 41 days

7.

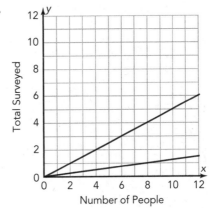

a. The number of unprotected people would be 160 and the number of sunburned people would be 40.
b. 160 people were surveyed
c. The number would only be equal for 0 people surveyed. The two lines never meet.

9.

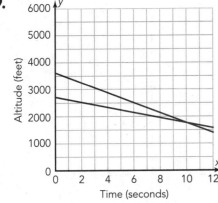

a. The first skydiver will be at 1465 feet and the second skydiver will be at 1195 feet.
b. 5 seconds
c. 10 seconds

11.

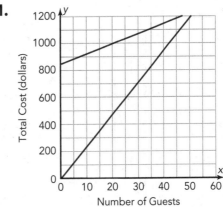

a. Option #1 will cost $1137.50 and Option #2 will cost $926.25.
b. 80 people
c. 52 people

13.

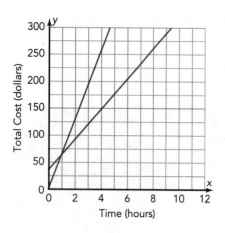

a. The first plumber's cost would be $148 and the second plumber's costs would be $256.

b. 5 hours

c. 1 hour

15.

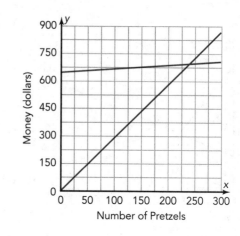

a. The cost is $656 and the income is $116.

b. 90 pretzels

c. 240 pretzels

II. A.

1. one solution; (2.25, 6)

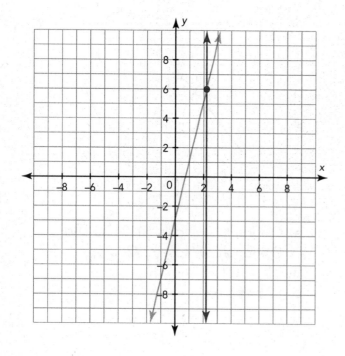

3. infinite solutions

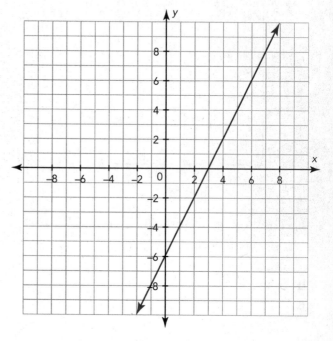

5. one solution; (5, −10)

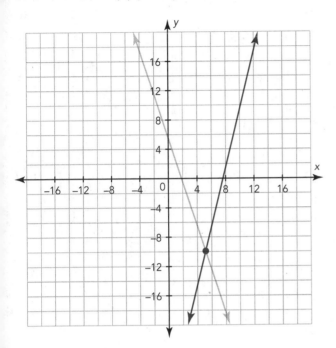

7. one solution; (−4, 5)

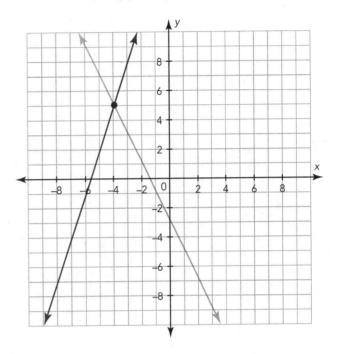

9. infinite solutions

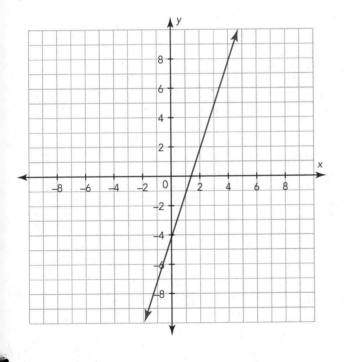

11. one solution; (−8, −1)

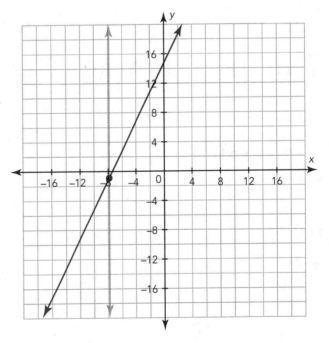

13. one solution; (−2, 0)

15. infinite solutions

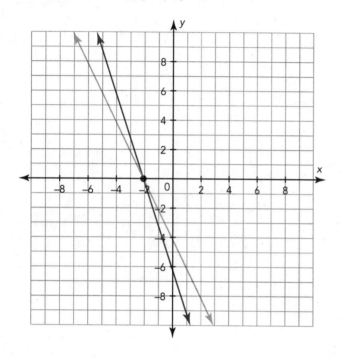

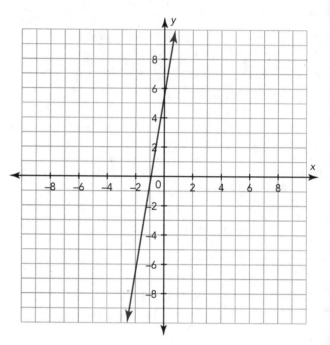

MODULE 4

Topic 1

The Real Number System

I. A.

1. not a perfect square

3. perfect square; 7 × 7

5. perfect square; 11 × 11

7. perfect square; 20 × 20

I. B.

1. 8

3. 9

5. 2

7. 5

I. C.

1. 11.4   **3.** 9.2   **5.** 4.9

I. D.

1. rational   **3.** irrational   **5.** irrational

7. rational   **9.** rational   **11.** irrational

II. A

1.

3.

5.

III. A

1.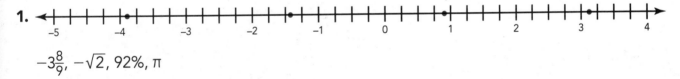

$-3\frac{8}{9}, -\sqrt{2}, 92\%, \pi$

3.

$143\%, \sqrt{4}, 2.7, \pi$

5.

$\frac{5}{8}, \sqrt{2}, \pi, 5.67$

Topic 2

The Pythagorean Theorem

I. A.

1. $c = 30$

3. $13.75 \approx b$

5. $c = 2.5$

7. $6.93 \approx b$

9. $c \approx 18.97$

11. $13.42 \approx b$

II. A.

1. 10 feet

3. 12.12 feet

5. 19.24 feet

7. 12.65 feet

9. 10.77 feet

11. 23 feet

III. A.

1. 10 units

3. $\sqrt{145}$ units

5. $\sqrt{394}$ units

7. 13 units

9. $\sqrt{136}$ units

11. $\sqrt{45}$ units

MODULE 5

Topic 1

Exponents and Scientific Notation

I. A.

1. $38n^6m^{12}$

3. $-15n^8z^{15}$

5. $\frac{5m^6d^3}{11}$

7. $-\frac{4k^3}{c}$

9. $\frac{9}{16za}$

11. $-\frac{1}{n^4m^2}$

13. $-88w^9d^9$

15. $54k^{13}m^{10}$

17. $\frac{2c^5}{b}$

II. A.

1. m^{24}

3. d^{25}

5. z^{10}

7. y^{16}

9. b^{15}

11. f^{21}

13. k^{12}

15. s^{40}

17. u^{14}

III. A.

1. $27d^{21}x^9$

3. $k^8w^{18}x^2$

5. $\dfrac{x^{21}}{c^{21}}$

7. $-64a^{15}y^6k^{15}$

9. $36y^4z^{18}$

11. $\dfrac{a^9}{d^{18}}$

13. $a^{16}x^{14}b^6$

15. $\dfrac{k^{15}}{c^3}$

17. $\dfrac{n^{12}}{b^{14}}$

IV. A.

1. $-\dfrac{11}{n^4}$

3. $5y^4$

5. $\dfrac{17}{z^7}$

7. $\dfrac{16}{19}$

9. $\dfrac{3}{x^4}$

11. $-\dfrac{6d^2}{5}$

13. -20

15. $-\dfrac{3}{2}$

17. $-2b$

V. A.

1. 8.52×10^5

3. 3×10^4

5. 7.35×10^7

7. 8.84×10^8

9. 9.54×10^6

11. 9.64×10^{-1}

13. 8×10^{-3}

15. 3.06×10^{-1}

17. 4×10^{-6}

V. B.

1. 30,000

3. 0.0002

5. 133,000

7. 6,000,000,000

9. 0.005

11. 0.000956

13. 90,000,000

15. 0.0000001

17. 509,000

VI. A.

1. >

3. >

5. <

7. >

9. <

11. >

VI. B.

1. 6.7

3. 104,000

5. 427

7. 226

9. 500,000,000

11. 8.2

Topic 2

Volume of Curved Figures

I. A.

1. 167,000 cubic millimeters

3. 4.2 inches

5. 2714.3 cubic inches

7. 1143.6 cubic inches

9. 254.9 inches

11. 1975.6 cubic feet

13. 939.4 cubic feet

15. 3.9 centimeters

II. A.

1. 122.6 cubic millimeters

3. 430.2 cubic feet

5. 3053.6 cubic inches

7. 6902 cubic feet

9. 56.5 cubic millimeters

11. 1583.9 cubic feet

13. 6330.4 cubic millimeters

15. 525.7 cubic inches

III. A.

1. 6.6 inches

3. 205,367.6 cubic millimeters

5. 20 centimeters

7. 44,602.2 cubic meters

9. 10.5 centimeters

11. 38,792.4 cubic centimeters

13. 21.6 millimeters

15. 2144.7 cubic inches